Situationa Matters!

Volume 1

Fifty lessons to improve situational awareness and high risk decision making

DR. RICHARD B. GASAWAY

Situational Awareness Matters! Volume 1/
by Richard B. Gasaway, Ph.D.
Gasaway Consulting Group, LLC
1769 Lexington Avenue North, Suite 177
St. Paul, MN 55113-6522
Phone: 612-548-4424

Situational Awareness Matters!
www.SAMatters.com

ISBN-10: 1939571081
ISBN-13: 978-1-939571-08-3

Cover Photo courtesy of
John M. Buckman, III
Chief Photographer
WildFire Studios

Printed in the United States of America by
Gasaway Consulting Group LLC.

CONTENTS

PREFACE:
WELCOME TO SITUATIONAL AWARENESS MATTERS!
VOLUME 1

The chapters in this book are a collection of articles I have written on my website, Situational Awareness Matters! The website is completely dedicated to my mission: Helping first responders see the bad things coming in time to change the outcome.

To say that situational awareness is important for first responders is a gross understatement. It is the leading cause of near miss events and the leading contributing factor for casualty events.

The motivation for my work comes from the thousands of dedicated men and women serving on the line to protect their communities every day. I am truly humbled to play a small part in helping to protect the protectors.

I have dedicated more than ten years of my life to the study of the art and science of decision making and to learn as much as I possibly can about situational awareness in the high-risk, high-consequence decision making environments of first responders, aviation, medicine, military, nuclear energy and others.

My desire to improve first responder situational awareness has consumed me. I am both an active researcher and a practitioner on this subject. In addition to my direct first responder experience of 30+ years, I also completed my doctoral research on first responder decision making and situational awareness.

At one time in my career I thought I knew all about situational awareness and how to make good decisions until I went back to school and studied the neuroanatomy and cognitive psychology behind it... and there is A LOT more behind it than I ever thought possible. And every day, I'm learning something new that I want to share with the community of my first responder brothers and sisters.

The Situational Awareness Matters platform (website, articles, podcast, books, videos and live programs) will be my forum to share what I have learned. I hope you will come along with me on this journey and be willing to participate so we can learn from each other while keeping our #1 goal in mind... doing everything we can to keep first responders safe.

How to use this book

The chapters in this book address situational awareness/decision making challenges and include proposed solutions. The solutions I offer are among many possible solutions you may consider.

Where appropriate, some chapters include a discussion segment to help guide conversations during training sessions or coffee table sessions.

1-FREELANCING

For many public safety agencies it is standard practice for the first arriving personnel (or crews of personnel) to deploy independently. Oftentimes these responders are highly trained, highly motivated and action oriented. What they are lacking is coordination of their efforts.

It is unrealistic to think multiple individuals (or crews) can arrive at varied times and make the same assessment of the situation/conditions and know, automatically, what every other team member is thinking and doing. Can you see how this could spell trouble?

Even professional football teams, who practice plays repetitively have the benefit of someone coordinating their actions. Imagine the impact on success if a football team had no quarterback to call the plays. (I know some of you are thinking of YOUR favorite team right now... and that's just funny).

But seriously, it is very beneficial when someone keeps the big picture view right from the beginning of the incident and coordinates the actions of the others incoming. Otherwise, the incident has the potential to degrade as the independent, uncoordinated actions of responders fail to achieve a common goal.

A Solution

Develop a standard operating guideline/policy that requires the first-arriving supervisor to assume the position as the person in charge and have that person maintain a "big picture" view of the incident. Allow some variation for imminent rescue situations. This person then becomes the coordinator of other incoming personnel. If they are a junior supervisor, they can be relieved of their command on the arrival of a more senior incident commander.

Discussion

1. Do your responders ever engage in independent actions at emergency scenes?

2. What things do they do to help reduce the impact of flawed team situational awareness?

2-STAFFING LEVELS

Research has demonstrated that, without question, stress narrows attention. Stress also erodes situational awareness and can impact decision making. One of the leading causes of stress that came from my research with foreground commanders were issues related to staffing with the most critical staffing stressor being understaffing.

If a commander arrives at the scene of an incident where much needs to be done (heavy workload) and the staffing is limited, the commander's stress will go up. This can have several catastrophic effects on the commander's situational awareness not the least being a narrowing of attention to that which causes the greatest stress. This is usually the crews that have been engaged in the high-risk, high-consequence activities. There may be additional stress if there is not adequate back-up resources on-scene in case something goes wrong.

As the commander's stress rises and attention narrows, the commander can miss very important things happening around him. This can be visual or audible information critical to good decision making.

A Solution

As with so many matters that relate to improving situational awareness, one of the first things is to be alert to the potential for narrowing attention as stress goes up. A commander can have a checklist available that provides reminders of the most important information to be captured and processed. The commander could consider alternate tactics until enough help arrives to safely get the job done.

Given the Type-A, aggressive, competitive nature of first responders, this can be a challenging task for command decision makers. Nonetheless, sometimes it is the most important decision a commander can make... the decision to be defensive when appropriate.

Discussion

1. Has staffing ever increased your stress and narrowed your attention?

2. Has your department engaged in aggressive high-risk, high-consequence operations without adequate staffing?

3. What do you do to improve your situational awareness as your stress level rises?

3-FATIGUE

Research has shown that fatigue can impact situational awareness in disturbing ways. Some responders think if they take a "safety nap" that will help. In a small way, it may, as any rest is better than no rest. However, a nap does not resolve systemic fatigue. Rest is a critical component to brain function and when there is not adequate rest or disrupted sleep, the impact is real, and measurable.

Some scientists have described the behavior of research participants suffering from fatigue as displaying the same qualities as a person who is intoxicated. When you think about the critical nature of first responder decision making, fatigue can have catastrophic effects.

The schedule of some public safety providers are not conducive to adequate rest. Twenty-four hour shifts in organizations who are busy service providers can present some real challenges to situational awareness, decision making and problem solving.

I have talked to many providers who admit the quality of their care and decisions may not be as good at night as it is during the day. Add the additional fatigue of working a forty-eight hour consecutive shift and it can compound the problem.

Responders may believe if they feel physically rested, they are mentally rested. In reality, when the physical body rests, the brain does not rest. In fact, the brain is surprisingly active while the body rests... suggesting the body rests so the brain may have access to the glucose (energy) to do it's heavy lifting. And what is the brain doing while you sleep?

Research with laboratory rats suggests the brain is sorting through all the data from the previous waking period, cataloging the events for future use. Hence, fatigue can not only impact short-term performance and memory, it can also impact long-term recall.

Got a perplexing problem? Sleeping on it really does help!

A Solution

Responders who work long hours must be provided with opportunities to rest their brains. It's not a matter of being lazy as some elected town hall dwellers may suggest. It's a matter of personal safety and quality of care to the citizens they serve.

Discussion

1. Do you think your situational awareness and decision quality is impacted when you are fatigued?

2. What are some ideas you can share about how to obtain adequate rest while working extended shifts?

3. What ideas do you have about getting adequate rest when off-duty?

4-CANCELING THE MAYDAY

I had an amazing conversation with a firefighter last night about situational awareness at my program in Brainerd, Minnesota and I just have to share it with you. He asked how many of the 26 fire departments represented in the room had a process in their mayday/rapid intervention procedures for how to cancel a mayday. Hearing the answer... I was stunned!

In all my travels and in all my teaching, I've never considered the ramifications of what could happen if there were no process by which to confirm a rescue has been completed (i.e. members who actually called the mayday were rescued) and the mayday should be cancelled. It was a brilliant question.

He shared with the class that he had posted the question on a national forum and found only a handful of departments that actually have a process to confirm a rescue is complete and the mayday is cancelled.

Absent this process, how do we really know the firefighters are safe and the right crew has been rescued, and all the firefighters in danger have been rescued. Imagine how complicated things could become if there were multiple maydays.

I am reminded of the Bricelyn Street fire in Pittsburgh, Pennsylvania and the valuable lessons that arose from the need to have good accountability during a mayday operation.

A Solution

Develop a procedure and train firefighters how to account for everyone and include a process for how to ensure the right firefighters have been rescued. The mayday procedure should include a process for how to cancel the mayday once the incident has de-escalated or, in the worst of possible outcomes, the commander determines the progression of the fire has exceeded the capacity of firefighting teams to conduct interior rescue operations.

Discussion

1. Does your department have both a mayday and a rapid intervention team (RIT) policy?

2. Do your mayday and RIT programs include a process for de-escalation of the mayday?

3. Have you ever been involved in a mayday operation? If so, share your experience of what went well and what could have been improved.

5 - KNOW YOUR EQUIPMENT

I recently received an email from a firefighter who was frustrated, disappointed and angry. He came to work for his shift and, as he always does, started his day by performing a safety check of his personal gear and his self-contained breathing apparatus (SCBA). When he opened the cabinet door on the apparatus he could hardly believe his eyes.

There, staring back at him was a brand new SCBA – a brand different than before with functionality completely different than his previous SCBA. He had received no notification, let alone any training on how to use this new piece of critical equipment. It was left for him to figure out on his own.

Such an act of incompetence on the part of this department's senior management, command staff and training staff seems unconscionable but it happened. This firefighter was left to fend for himself and to teach himself (quickly) how to use this new SCBA. Were all the other firefighters on his department going to do the same? Who knows?

Situational awareness requires a conscious effort to capture the clues and cues in an often hectic and hostile environment. When responders have to focus so much cognitive energy on how to operate their equipment, their situational awareness is going to be impacted.

A Solution

No equipment should ever be placed into service without a comprehensive orientation session and the opportunity to use the equipment in a practice/training mode.

Confidence with how to use equipment and knowing its limitations is essential to responder safety. On the emergency scene is not the place to learn these lessons.

Discussion

1. What is the process your department uses to ensure members are familiar with new equipment before it is placed into service?

2. If you've put new SCBA into service in the recent past, share what steps your department used to endure a proper orientation of your members?

3. Have you ever witnesses a near-miss event because a first responder was not completely familiar with the operation of their equipment?

6-RADIO COMMUNICATIONS

I was invited to be an observer at a regional police tactical training exercise. The program was a multi-day event, starting with some classroom training and culminating in a series of simulations using mock weapons, flash-bangs and actors. The one thing that readily stood out to me was the tactical teams were not using radios to communicate.

I asked the training coordinator why the teams were not using radios and was told the radios from the many different agencies represented were not compatible and they didn't have enough radios for the teams to be properly equipped so they decided to run the exercises without radios.

The lack of coordination and challenges with communications were readily apparent and it definitely impacted the situational awareness of teams who were observed engaging in independent action, unaware of the activities of other teams.

At one point, a flash bang device was deployed and detonated dangerously close to a member of another team. It was definitely a near-miss event by all calculations.

After the training was completed I had the opportunity to have a brief discussion with the coordinator and asked what contributes to the greatest challenges to tactical teams at real events. The answer was "communications." Interestingly, there were no training sessions at this symposium dedicated to the topic of communications – the self-admitted leading challenge to team success.

A Solution

First responder teams would find great benefit in having a discussion about what causes the greatest challenges to success and what factors routinely contribute to safety concerns. Then, once identified, set a plan into action to fix the problem. Admittedly, training on radio communications is not nearly as exciting as donning gear, throwing flash bangs, kicking doors and taking down bad guys at gun point.

But when it comes to improving team coordination, safety and situational awareness, it may be one of the most important skills a first responder can possess. Practice effective communications to improve safety.

Interestingly, when responders practice high-stress scenarios without radios, they are at risk of not using the radios properly (or at all) during real scenarios because of their failure to use them in practice. Remember: Practice does not make perfect. Practice makes permanent.

Discussion

1. How often does your organization build radio training into tactical evolutions?

2. Does your organization teach members how to effectively talk on the radio during high-stress, high-consequence events?

3. Do you have a standard operating guideline about how to talk on the radio and how to determine what information is essential radio traffic (i.e., how to manage the "noise" on the radio)?

4. What best practices are you aware of about how to effectively communicate on the radio?

7-SHARED SITUATIONAL AWARENESS

Shared situational awareness simply means two or more people have a commonly understood mental model (mental image of what's happening... and what is going to happen in the future). When responders arrive at the scene of an emergency at different times (which is common), there is a risk that each person arriving will have a different understanding of what is happening because the information (clues and cues) have changed.

This can put responders at risk if they think they have a common understanding of what's going on, when in reality, they don't because the information has changed.

Think about a time when you may have arrived ten minutes late, after a movie started. Those who have been in the theater from the beginning have a different understanding of what's going on than you have because they benefited from capturing all of the clues and cues from the start. Unless you get a briefing, you are going to be at a disadvantage.

A Solution

An incident with one person defined as the commander who has watched the big picture incident (and all its changes from the start), in real-time, will likely have the best situational awareness. This person will also have a good understanding of the "speed" of the incident – a critical component to ensuring responder safety.

The commander, or their designee, can provide progress and update reports for other responding units and provide critical information to responders as they arrive. It is very difficult to have shared situational awareness when newly arriving responders think they know what's going on when, in fact, they are clueless (literally).

Discussion

1. How does your department ensure that all responders are on the same page when they arrive at different times?

2. What are the most critical pieces of information that responders need to know when they arrive that will improve their situational awareness?

3. What is at risk if responders arrive at different times and "assume" they know what's going on, only to find out they were clueless?

8-YOUR RATIONAL BRAIN

Oftentimes during my programs on situational awareness and decision making I have participants share stories of incidents they have responded to, or incidents they have read about, or videos of incidents they have watched. This happened recently during a program where Jeff, a firefighter with 20+ years of experience asked me: "How could they be so stupid? Everyone knows you don't do that!"

Such statements are made by participants who are using their rational brain in a low stress, no consequence (classroom) environment. In these conditions it is easy to see behavior that appears to be foolish or in contempt of good safety practices. It is also easy to criticize the performance of others.

I encourage my participants to stop judging the performance of others and start being a student of human behavior.

As my students begin to understand how vulnerable the rational human brain is toward making bad decisions under stress, and more importantly the reason behind these seemingly poor decisions, their entire perspective begins to change.

In fact, after I help attendees understand the "how and why" of decision making under stress, the very people who were critics begin to see they are as vulnerable to making a bad decision as the person in the video or case study.

I love it when a room full of people get an "ah huh" moment. Thanks Jeff for asking the question that set up a great discussion on how the brain makes decisions under stress.

9-IT'S MORE THAN "PAYING ATTENTION"

If you want to improve your situational awareness, just pay better attention!

Really? Oh my goodness.

No! It is hardly that simple.

I just read an article where the author was giving advice about how to improve situational awareness. He said that situational awareness can be improved by paying better attention. At the very most basic level, that is true.

It has taken me over seven years of research and earning a doctoral degree on the subject to even begin understanding the complexities of the brain and how behavior changes under stress. Situational awareness is NOT as simple as paying better attention.

But those who don't understand the complexities of situational awareness and the neuroscience behind attentiveness offer this very simplistic advice if, for no other reason than they don't know any better. In their defense, that's where I was ten years ago. But not any more.

It takes a full day of training for me to help first responders understand how to develop and maintain situational awareness and make a quality decision under stress.

Don't be fooled by simple people giving simple advice and simple solutions to complex problems. There are over Fifty Ways to Kill a First Responder from flawed situational awareness.

A Solution

Be sure that when you are learning about situational awareness in high-stress, high-consequence environments that you are learning from credible experts who understand the neuroscience behind how decisions are made.

There are a lot of resources out there for you to improve your understanding on this incredibly important first responder safety topic.

You can get it from me... or you can get it from someone else. The important thing is... you get it... and you don't let a novice teach you how to be an expert. There's too much at stake to be set-up for failure.

Discussion

1. Where have you found credible sources about how to develop and maintain situational awareness in high-stress, high-consequence environments?

2. Have you ever watched a video or read a casualty report where firefighters were hurt or killed and thought they may have avoided the catastrophic outcome if they'd just paid better attention?

3. Describe what factors have contributed to the erosion of situational awareness.

10-SOPS CAN HARM DECISION MAKING

I am a big advocate of departments having standardized procedures to guide operations as tools to help develop and maintain situational awareness. I don't really care if you call them Standard Operating Procedures (SOPs) or Standard Operating Guidelines (SOGs). The important thing is you have a set of commonly understood Standards that guide performance.

Standards are especially beneficial in high-stress, high-consequence situations that first responders often find themselves in. However, the very Standards that are written to keep first responders safe can also contribute to catastrophic outcomes. Here's how...

Oftentimes department training officers set up scenarios where responders perform to the scripted SOP. Nothing wrong with that. However, the training scenarios that are developed by well-intended training officers always result in success.

And, as all first responders know, the complexity of incidents can often require actions that are not consistent with the Standards.

Here's an example. A department has a Mayday Standard and a Rapid Intervention Standard. The training staff develops an evolution where a crew member gets into trouble and calls a Mayday. In the Mayday report, the distressed crew member provides a LUNAR Report:

L - location, in the fire building

U - unit, company designation and assignment

N - name(s), of person(s) requiring assistance

A - air supply, remaining

R - resources, needed

The Rapid Intervention Team springs into action, locating the distressed firefighter and helping them to safety. The drill is repeated several times to ensure competency.

In my Fireground Mistakes and Best Practices program, I ask firefighters if they have participated in training evolutions like this and many acknowledge they have. That gives me encouragement.

Then, I ask the firefighters how many times the distressed firefighters gave incomplete LUNAR reports, inaccurate LUNAR reports, or no LUNAR reports during the training evolution. Silence befalls the room. The evolutions always have the distressed crews giving LUNAR reports and they are always complete and accurate. That's too bad. Because the harsh reality of the real world is complete and accurate information may not be provided.

If you do not build failure into your evolutions, you may be training for failure. And the worst part about it… you may not even realize you're heading toward disaster because you're so focused on training for success.

In my Mental Management of Emergencies Program, I demonstrate through a series of exercises that stress can cause a person to leave out important details and, incredibly, make up information.

I don't want to say they lie, but they can say some things that are pretty outlandish. Anyone who's attended the Mental Management program knows what I'm talking about. We can have fun in the classroom demonstrating the shortcomings of the stressed brain but on the emergency scene, it can be catastrophic.

A Solution

It is important that Mayday and RIT practice include evolutions where information is incomplete or inaccurate so that crews learn how to improvise. The buzz word for this is Managing the Unexpected. I call it being a Resilient Problem Solver. Call it what you will, but responders need to be able to think quickly on their feet when things are not going to plan (as often happens during a Mayday).

The more they practice solving novel problems in training, the better they will become at solving novel problems in real emergencies.

In an upcoming chapter I'm going to share with you why you'll want to be sure failure is built into training evolutions. Here's a hint: It's not to give supervisors a reason to discipline or responders a reason to have low self-esteem. It's to rewire the brain for success! Stay tuned...

Discussion

1. Does your department have Mayday and Rapid Intervention Standards?

2. How often do you practice performing rescues?

3. How does your department build complexity into your Mayday and Rapid Intervention evolutions?

11-SETTING EXPECTATIONS

Situational Awareness is developed, maintained, erodes, and is regained at three levels. The highest level of situational awareness is developed from being able to make realistic and accurate projections of the future events. The projections are sometimes called "mental models." Projecting the future facilitates being able to see bad things coming... in time to change the outcome.

If there was ever a theme that runs through everything I teach in my classes about situational awareness it is just that: Being able to see the bad things coming in time to change the outcome.

One of the best ways to see the bad things coming is by forming expectations about the future outcomes of the activities happening at the emergency scene. When a crew is given a task there should be two expectations that arise from the assignment:

1. What will the successful outcome look like as a result of the crew's performance?

2. How long should it take the crew to get that task done?

Thinking in terms of a successful outcome keeps the focus on the purpose of the crew's assignment as it relates to the overall incident action plan.

How long it should take for a task to be completed is based on many factors. It is important to place a time expectation on task completion, especially if the conditions of the incident are fast-moving and deteriorating.

The highest level of situational awareness... projection... predicting the future... is based on setting realistic and accurate expectations.

A Solution

Part of the size-up should include thinking about the future. Not only what it will look like, but how much time it should take to look that way.

If the expectation is something should happen within five minutes, it is at the five minute mark that an assessment of the progress should be completed. Does the incident look like it should? If not, why? And more importantly if not, what should be done about it that will ensure the safety of personnel operating in the high-risk environment.

Discussion

1. If an incident is deteriorating, why would a commander continue to allow personnel to perform high-risk, high-consequence activities when it appears things are heading toward disaster?

2. Why is it so hard for emergency response personnel to change gears and go in a new direction once an aggressive action plan is in motion?

3. What are some best practices for how to assess progress against expectations?

12-MULTITASKING

If a picture is worth a thousand words, a live demonstration may be worth ten thousand words. In a recent situational awareness and decision making class I was explaining to the participants the science behind why humans are such poor multitaskers.

If course, when I do this there is always someone in the class who, for whatever reason, thinks they're great at multitasking. I love it when this happens because I'm prepared.

For this scenario I set up an exercise where two people get to role play being in charge of an emergency. One of them is going to multitask (guess which one gets that dubious honor?) and the other one gets to perform only a single task.

The multitasking person has to perform the same activities as the single tasking person and one additional (physical activity). The results are always predictable... a train wreck.

The single tasking person's performance is always nearly flawless while the performance of my multitasking participant always turns into a disaster. The multitasker forgets about 90% of the data they were supposed to remember and their performance is fraught with error. It's sad and unfortunate.

The simple fact is, the conscious human brain cannot multitask, plain and simple. This is backed up by science and the analysis of functional magnetic resonance imaging (fMRI) data.

Responders can be lulled into believing they are good multitaskers because they do it so often with so little consequence that it gives them the confidence to think they are good at it. Where, in reality, they're not good at it and luck is the only thing standing in the way of a disaster.

A Solution

Concede to the vulnerabilities of the human brain. Acknowledge that multitasking is a myth and avoid it by focusing on performing one critical task at a time.

Proper staffing plays a big role in efforts to avoid multitasking. Preloading an incident with the proper number of responders will reduce the exposure to the need to perform multiple concurrent tasks.

Discussion

1. Why do people think they are good multitaskers when, in fact, their brain cannot multitask at all?

2. What can first responders do to avoid multitasking during high-stress, high-consequence operational periods?

3. Describe how your situational awareness has been impacted by multitasking.

13-THE WALKING PAR

Personnel Accountability Reports (PARs) are essential to helping commanders develop and maintain situational awareness. A quality PAR dials the commander into every crew's size, their location and their progress. But the standard PAR has a fundamental flaw that can adversely impact the commander's situational awareness.

Summertime can bring excessive heat and humidity to many regions. When weather is severe, first response personnel can be especially vulnerable to heat-related medical emergencies. It is possible that crews heavily focused on task performance may not be aware of how the heat is impacting them.

In excessive weather, a standard roll-call PAR may not be sufficient if it only assesses crew size, location and task performance/progress. Crews suffering physically from outside heat may find themselves affirming PAR without thinking about how the heat has impacted their stamina.

And even if they are aware of how the heat has impacted them, the standard PAR provides no way for the crew to tip command on their condition.

A Solution

In excessive heat the standard radio roll-call PAR may not effectively assess the physical well-being of crews. When a crew acknowledges PAR, it speaks nothing to their welfare (physical condition and stamina).

It may be beneficial to ask safety officers to conduct a "Walking Par" and visually assess each firefighter's well-being with their own eyes.

Alternatively, PAR reports could include a code that indicated the crew's physical well-being. For example:

<u>Green</u>: Crew is in an excellent state of readiness.
<u>Yellow</u>: Crew has been actively performing high-stress tasks and has reduced stamina.
<u>Red</u>: Crew has been extensively performing high-stress tasks and has little stamina remaining.

Command conducting a PAR might hear reports like this:

Engine 101, PAR, Crew of 4 green, second floor, attacking the fire.

Truck 302, PAR, crew of 4. 2 green, 2 yellow, third floor conducting a search

Squad 211, PAR, crew of 4 yellow, on the first floor conducting a search.

Engine 17, PAR, crew of 4 red, in staging.

There are 6 firefighters at full-stamina, 6 firefighters running on half-stamina, and 4 firefighters who are, essentially, out-of-service.

A system (like color coding) could tell the commander a whole lot more about the physical stamina of crews, improving the commander's situational awareness.

Discussion

1. Does your department have a process to assess the physical well-being of personnel operating in high-stress, high-consequence environments?

2. What can you do to ensure the well-being of personnel during periods of excessive weather?

3. In addition to a Walking Par or a coding system, how can the well-being of firefighters be assessed?

14-EXPECTING THE UNEXPECTED

The advice "expect the unexpected" can lead to a great deal of criticism. For example, if one can expect something to happen, then it is (technically) no longer unexpected... and so on. Setting all the hair-splitting aside, to expect the unexpected is to anticipate the possibilities of events occurring in advance of them actually occurring.

For example, if you are preparing to drive somewhere during the rush hour you can expect the possibility of minor accidents and delays and plan accordingly by leaving early, taking another route, or having an alternative route in mind that you can take if you encounter problems. The mere act of thinking about traffic problems in advance can improve situational awareness because it can help you capture clues about what is on the horizon.

Recently in a class I was talking about this and one of the participants shared a story of an incident where firefighters responded to a "routine" wires down call. The details of the incident are detailed on an excellent website, www.vententersearch.com. Visit the site to view the story of how the fire crew was able to expect the unexpected and avoid an electrical shock.

The conversation in class came on the heels of my sharing the details of a LODD where a firefighter exited the apparatus after arriving on the scene of a brush fire (not a wires down call... a brush fire). As it was a "routine" brush fire on the side of the road, the crew probable already had it in their minds that the brush fire had been started by a discarded cigarette. It's not only a plausible explanation for the cause, it is what we see most often.

The crew did not expect the unexpected. The brush fire was caused by a downed power line... not a cigarette. The line was no longer arcing when the crew arrived. It was dark outside and none of the firefighters saw the power line. A firefighter stepped on it and died.

A Solution

Instead of giving the advice to expect the unexpected, I am going to recommend that responders anticipate the unusual. In other words, when you're responding to or arriving at a scene be mindful of the factors that could be contributing to the problem that are out of the ordinary – the non-routine. The best way to get to thinking in this mindset is to set up scenarios for training and have responders brainstorm the possible causes and consequences. Think of it as seeing the end result of the event in advance and not being surprised by whatever comes your way because you were able to anticipate things.

Discussion

1. What are some examples of unusual incidents you have responded to that caught you underprepared for what happened? What did you learn from it? What would you do differently now to be better prepared?

2. Sometimes the unexpected is disguised by clues that are absent (it's what you don't see that is the real clue that there's a problem). Share some experiences you've had where the absence of certain clues was the real indicator there was a problem.

15-META AWARENESS

Meta awareness means being consciously aware of your own awareness. I know that sounds redundant, so let me explain. One of the things responders need to understand is situational awareness is fragile. Situational awareness erodes in ways that are so subtle that it may erode before a responder even realizes it is gone. The solution may be in developing meta awareness.

In order to have situational awareness, it is first important to understand what it is and how to develop it. Situational awareness is developed by capturing clues and cues (called perception). Then the clues and cues are processed into meaning (called comprehension). Finally, the highest level of situational awareness is predicting the future events.

To have meta awareness means being consciously aware of whether you are doing all three (perception, comprehension and projection).

When you're busy performing tasks in a high-stress, high-consequence environment it can be difficult to remember the process to develop and maintain situational awareness. Reminding yourself of the levels of SA is a powerful way to help you maintain it.

A Solution

You can develop meta awareness several ways. The easiest way is to create a visual prompt, like having "How is my situational awareness?" written on your command worksheet. Better yet, list all three steps and continually ask yourself how you're doing.

Alternatively, you can memorize and practice mental situational awareness prompts. To be able to do this, you'll need to memorize the levels and rehearse it so often that you can recite them as quickly as the alphabet.

Discussion

1. What would you expect to be the first indication you are losing your situational awareness at an emergency scene?

2. If you thought you were losing your situational awareness, what would you do to regain it?

3. Which level of situational awareness do you think causes the most problems? Why?

16-DISTRACTIONS AND INTERRUPTIONS

As I talk with first responders in classes about the impact of distractions and interruptions on situational awareness I find myself often being asked: What's the difference? While there are distinctly different causes for distractions and interruptions, the outcome is often very similar... a reduction in situational awareness and the potential for a catastrophic outcome.

A distraction is something that draws one's attention away from what they are supposed to be paying attention to, entirely unintentionally. For example, a responder working at a scene might be distracted by a loud noise (e.g., an air horn, siren, a scream or an explosion). This draws the attention of the responder to the source of the noise (though it doesn't have to be a noise... it could just as easily be something visual or a smell). While the responder's attention is focused on the sources of the distraction, however brief, attention is drawn away from what he or she was giving attention to just prior to the distraction.

An interruption is something that draws one's attention away from what they are supposed to be paying attention to entirely on purpose. For example, a responder working at a scene might be interrupted by someone talking to him or her, by being called on the radio or by receiving a cell phone call. The interruption draws the attention of the responder away. However brief, attention is refocused on something new.

The reason distractions and interruptions are so dangerous for responders are multiple fold. First, emergency scenes are fertile ground for distractions and interruptions. There are often loud noises, bright lights and lots of things to stimulate the visual and audible senses. Second, responders like to share information and this is often done by radio or face-to-face communications.

Each interaction is, without passing judgment on how important it may be, an interruption to the receiver's thought process.

Every time a thought is disrupted by a distraction or interruption, the brain leaves one thought behind to pick up on the new one.

When this happens, situational awareness is at risk because the return to the original thought may not be to the exact place where the thought was left.

Or, even more dangerous, it's possible the brain may never come back to the original thought at all, even though that original thought may have involved the performance of a critical safety task.

A Solution

The best way to avoid the impact of distractions and interruptions is to reduce exposure to them. If commanding this incident, this can be accomplished by being physically remote from direct contact to those stimuli that distract and interrupt. This may mean commanding from a short distance away from the action or commanding from within a vehicle.

For operational personnel, consider assigning one person to listen to one radio, versus having the entire company listen to every radio transmission and risk having the entire crew being mentally drawn off task. Remember a radio transmission is an interruption.

Try to avoid having the entire company drawn off task to listen to a radio transmission that may not even pertain to their assignment. And while consideration needs to be given to avoiding tunneled senses, it is important to stay focused on the task.

Discussion

1. Describe an incident scene where you were distracted by something visual or audible. How did it impact your ability to stay focused on your task?

2. What are some tips and tricks you use to control distractions and interruptions while operating on stimulus-rich emergency scenes?

3. Are your commanders located remotely or in the thick of the action? What have you observed about their ability to maintain situational awareness based on where they are located?

17 - WHEN BUDGETS IMPACT STAFFING

Throughout the fire service there are departments whose staffing has been reduced as a result of budget cuts. That is not going to come as a shock to most readers. What has been shocking for me, however, has been the response to my question of what fire department leaders are doing to ensure the situational awareness and safety of line personnel as a result of these cutbacks.

As I have heard many, many stories in my fireground command decision making classes about staffing cuts, I am frequently in the position to inquire about how tactics have changed as a result of staffing reductions. I am both shocked and disappointed to learn that in many fire departments the command staff has not held meetings with line personnel to discuss how tactics will change as a result of having less personnel.

When I ask the line personnel what they're supposed to do differently, they have no idea. In fact, most of the time the response is "It's business as usual."

But it's not. If less personnel are responding or if the response times of personnel are going to be delayed then, tactically, the same amount of work cannot get done in the same amount of time and this can compromise firefighter safety.

Firefighters need to hear from commanders, in advance of an emergency, that the game plan is going to change and the new plan of attack should be shared. Otherwise firefighters will continue to do the same thing they've always done, only with less resources... and greater risk. A competent commander should never let this happen.

A Solution

If staffing levels have been reduced or are anticipated to be reduced, commanders need to meet with line personnel and run through scenarios of how strategies and tactics will change on a fire scene. A good way to do this is to run a scenario with the former staffing, detailing what crews do and the anticipated outcomes.

Then run the same scenario with reduced staffing and discuss how the workload changes and time for the completion of anticipated tasks changes (see the chapter on expectations for more on this).

Discussion

1. If your department has experienced a reduction in staffing, how have your tactics changed to reflect the reduction and to ensure firefighter safety?

2. Have your commanders sat down with crews and held meaningful discussions about how staffing impacts strategy and tactics and how they plan to change their approach to fire attack to ensure firefighter safety?

3. What fireground challenges from staffing reductions cause you the greatest concerns?

18-STOP THE INSANITY: PART 1

The training practices used in many communities are setting up emergency response personnel for failure and flawed situational awareness. The sad part is most don't even realize they're doing it. When casualties occur, so do investigations. The investigations result in recommendations for how to prevent future casualty events.

The National Institute of Occupational Safety and Health (NIOSH) published a report titled Preventing Risk and Injuries to Firefighters Using Risk Management Principles at Structure Fires. In the report, they chronicle several case studies. In order to keep my chapters short, I am going to parse this into four chapters. We'll start with the an excerpt from a LODD case study, followed by a listing of four (of many) NIOSH recommendations. In each chapter in this series, I will offer an assessment of how the firefighters were Trained for Failure and how this meets the definition of insanity (doing the same thing over and over again while expecting the results to be different).

The NIOSH Case Study

On February 19, 2005, a 39-year-old male career fire captain died after being trapped by the partial collapse of the roof on a vacant, one-story, wood frame dwelling. The 50 year old house was abandoned, in a dilapidated condition, and known by residents in the area to be a "crack house" at the time of the incident.

Crews arriving on the scene could see fire venting through the roof at the rear of the house, with some firefighters reporting that flames were well above the roofline. The victim was the captain on the first-arriving engine crew, which was assigned to perform a "fast attack": They were to take a hose line into the house, locate the seat of the fire, and begin to extinguish it. Thermal imaging cameras were available on scene but not used to locate the seat of the fire. The incident commander walked to the C-D corner of the burning house to size up the situation and determined that roof ventilation was not feasible because of the fire venting through the roof.

The victim and a firefighter advanced the initial attack line through the front entrance and made their way toward the rear of the house. Conditions deteriorated rapidly as they advanced toward the rear. The fast attack crew had just begun to direct water onto the burning ceiling in the kitchen and den areas when the roof at the rear of the structure collapsed, trapping the captain under burning debris.

The collapse pushed fire toward the front of the house. Soot and combustible dust particles suspended in the air were quickly ignited along with combustible gases, sending a fireball rolling toward the front of the structure. Before the collapse, two other crews had entered through the front. The rapidly deteriorating conditions following the collapse quickly engulfed the other crews with fire, and five firefighters received burns requiring medical attention.

The victim was pronounced dead on the scene by medical examiners [NIOSH 2005a]. The dilapidated condition of the abandoned structure, fire venting through the roof upon arrival, and deteriorating conditions encountered by the advancing interior crews as the fire escalated were all factors suggesting a more defensive strategy was in order.

The NIOSH Recommendations

NIOSH made many recommendations in their report. There are a few, however, that I would like to focus on to make my point of our insanity:

1. A thorough size-up and risk analysis should be performed before conducting operations in any burning structure.

2. Fire-fighting operations should be limited to defensive (exterior) strategy if the structure is judged to be unsafe and in any situation where the risks to firefighter safety are excessive.

3. Offensive (interior attack) operations should only be considered when sufficient resources are on scene to conduct offensive operations with a reasonable degree of safety, including the ability to perform essential support functions (i.e., water supply, ventilation, lighting, utility control, accountability, rapid intervention teams).

4. Additional size-ups and risk analyses should be performed before changing strategies, including any decision to conduct interior overhaul operations following a defensive fire attack.

Training For Failure

In my travels around this country teaching first responders, I have had the good fortune of seeing many training facilities. Most burn buildings I've encountered are made of steel, concrete or a combination of the two.

The fires are ignited from Class-A combustibles or propane and, for the most part, produce a consistent and predictable amount of smoke and fire. Let's see how that applies to casualty events.

NIOSH Recommendation #1

A thorough size-up and risk analysis should be performed before conducting operations in any burning structure.

Indeed! However, in order to ensure this will be done at a structure fire, it must be done during training burns. Not once or twice or on occasion. Rather, as the NIOSH report recommends, "in any burning structure." This means completing a thorough size-up and risk analysis before starting fire attack at every training fire as well. Do we do that? I can't speak for everyone, but I can tell you that I have observed MANY who do not.

Why not? Because the building is made of concrete and/or steel. There is no risk of the burn building falling down during the evolution.

Conducting a thorough size-up of the burn building might be perceived as a waste of time. It might even lead to criticism from firefighters who are anxious to take hose lines into burning buildings and put out fires.

This is an important point that cannot get lost here. It's one that I speak to extensively in my Mental Management of Emergencies classes. Practice does not make perfect. Practice makes permanent. If firefighters are not required to complete a thorough size-up prior to commencing interior operations at EVERY training evolution, their situational awareness will be flawed. Worse, they will not be building the process of completing a size-up into the habits formed through repetition. They are being Trained For Failure. To expect firefighters to perform at an emergency scene in a manner inconsistent with their training is INSANE! It won't happen.

19-STOP THE INSANITY: PART 2

Welcome to the second chapter in the four-part Stop The Insanity situational awareness series. In the previous chapter we discussed challenges with size-up. In this chapter, I'm going to discuss why firefighters fail to be defensive when the fire conditions indicate offensive operations are inappropriate.

The previous chapter sets up the discussion for this chapter. If you haven't read it yet, I encourage you to do so as it will improve your understanding of lessons I will be sharing here.

The training practices used in many communities are setting up emergency response personnel for failure and flawed situational awareness. The sad part is most don't even realize they're doing it. When casualties occur, so do investigations. The investigations result in recommendations for how to prevent future casualty events.

Training for Failure

As noted in the previous chapter, most burn buildings I've encountered are made of steel, concrete or a combination of the two. The fires are ignited from Class-A combustibles or propane and, for the most part, produce a consistent and predictable amount of smoke and fire. This may be good from the standpoint of safety, but it can cause some issues when it comes to teaching critical thinking and decision making skills.

NIOSH Recommendation #2

Fire-fighting operations should be limited to defensive (exterior) strategy if the structure is judged to be unsafe and in any situation where the risks to firefighter safety are excessive.

Indeed! However, while conducting training operations that involves fires in a concrete and/or steel building, the structure is never judged to be unsafe. Why? Because it was built to be burned in.

It's NOT going to fall down. If firefighters train repetitively in a building they know, with confidence, will not fall down on them, they will not be of the mindset to judge a structure fire unsafe.

During live fire training evolutions, firefighters are not learning what an unsafe building looks like. The burn building NEVER looks unsafe. I cannot speak for all fire departments but I can say that I have observed many who, for whatever reason, seem to skip the risk assessment step.

In addition to failing to train firefighters on what defensive conditions look like, many fire departments do not train firefighters on what to do, tactically, if they did encounter a defensive fire. Such tactics cannot be taken for granted nor can they simply be talked about. They must be practiced to build muscle memory. Muscles do not learn from verbal instructions. Muscles learn from muscle movement.

Failing to instruct firefighters on what a defensive fire looks like and what to do if/when they see one flaws situational awareness and it is Training For Failure. To expect firefighters to perform at an emergency scene in a manner inconsistent with their training is INSANE! It won't happen.

20-STOP THE INSANITY: PART 3

Welcome to the third chapter in the four-part Stop The Insanity series. The training practices used in many communities are setting up emergency response personnel for failure and flawed situational awareness. The sad part is most don't even realize they're doing it. When casualties occur, so do investigations. The investigations result in recommendations for how to prevent future casualty events.

Training for Failure

As noted in Chapter 18, most burn buildings I've encountered are made of steel, concrete or a combination of the two. The fires are ignited from Class-A combustibles or propane and, for the most part, produce a consistent and predictable amount of smoke and fire.

This may be good from the standpoint of safety, but it can cause some issues when it comes to teaching critical thinking and decision making skills.

NIOSH Recommendation #3

Offensive (interior attack) operations should only be considered when sufficient resources are on scene to conduct offensive operations with a reasonable degree of safety, including the ability to perform essential support functions (i.e., water supply, ventilation, lighting, utility control, accountability, rapid intervention teams).

Indeed! I am pleased to report that in my travels and observations, fire departments do a great job with this one, often assembling 15-45 firefighters at the burn building prior to commencing the training event. This improves safety, not to mention compliance with the NFPA 1403 burn standard. During training events it is easy to assemble 15+ members to immediately perform all the activities listed in the NIOSH recommendations. Easy... yes! Realistic... no!

And it gives firefighters a flawed sense of resource availability. It flaws expectations and it flaws situational awareness.

Once again, I cannot speak for all fire departments but from my observations, staffing is often in-place for ready and immediate deployment. When ventilation is called for, the vent team is sent. No delays.

Water supply issues? Never! The water is fully secured before the first flame is ever struck. As these challenges are engineered out of training by policy or standard, so go the challenges that firefighters will face during real structure fires. It's Training For Failure. To expect firefighters to perform at an emergency scene in a manner inconsistent with their training is INSANE! It won't happen.

Just once, I'd like to see an investigation report say: *Stop training your firefighters to do the things that are killing them.* Of course, that would require a knowledge that it's happening and best practices for how to correct it.

21-STOP THE INSANITY: PART 4

Welcome to the fourth and final chapter in the Stop The Insanity series. The training practices used in many communities are setting up emergency response personnel for failure and flawed situational awareness. The sad part is most don't even realize they're doing it. When casualties occur, so do investigations. The investigations result in recommendations for how to prevent future casualty events.

Training for Failure

As noted in Chapter 18, most burn buildings I've encountered are made of steel, concrete or a combination of the two. The fires are ignited from Class-A combustibles or propane and, for the most part, produce a consistent and predictable amount of smoke and fire.

This may be good from the standpoint of safety, but it can cause some issues when it comes to teaching critical thinking and decision making skills.

NIOSH Recommendation #4

Additional size-ups and risk analyses should be performed before changing strategies, including any decision to conduct interior overhaul operations following a defensive fire attack.

Indeed! The size-up should be on-going and a continual assessment should be made of changing conditions, the speed of the incident and how fast the structure is decomposing as a result of the heat and fire. The problem is during controlled fires in concrete and/or steel buildings, conditions do not mimic reality.

In fact, conditions hardly change at all – not just during the current evolution, but from evolution to evolution. As well, the speed of the incident does not change because the fire is not spreading room-to-room and the fire is not consuming the structural components of the building.

Finally, the burn building is not decomposing under the strain of the fire. It's built NOT to decompose!

Once again, I cannot speak for all fire departments but from my observations, live fire training in a burn building does not address the realistic challenges that will be faced at a structure fire. This leads to flawed situational awareness, a flawed sense of confidence based on repetitive successful outcomes, a flawed ability to assess changing conditions, a flawed ability to know when to be defensive and a flawed ability to know when (and how) to order the removal of firefighters from a structure fire in time to avoid the catastrophic outcome. It's Training For Failure. To expect firefighters to perform at an emergency scene in a manner inconsistent with their training is INSANE! It won't happen.

Just once, I'd like to see an investigation report say: *Stop training your firefighters to do the things that are killing them.* Of course, that would require a knowledge that it's happening and best practices for how to correct it.

22 - IMPROVING LEARNING AND RECALL

Is there a role for humor while training first responders on critical, life-saving, skills?

The flight attendant begins dolling out the obligatory, in fact, federally mandated, pre-flight safety instructions. If you're a frequent flyer, your situational awareness is probably pretty low. You know the routine and it's boring. If you're an infrequent flyer, the monotone, or should I say mono-drone voice of the lead flight attendant is enough to make you bury your eyes deep into the sky magazine. But, on this flight, something's different.

The flight attendant begins by saying:

"Our airline employs some of the safest pilots in the industry. Unfortunately, our flight today doesn't have any of them so you'd better fasten your seatbelt and play close attention to what I'm about to lay down. There may be fifty ways to leave your lover but there's only six ways to leave this airplane."

All eyes and ears were immediately fixated on the lead flight attendant. Trust me, I was on the flight and witnessed it first-hand. This was one of the best stand-up comedic routines I've seen in a long time. I enjoyed it. Wait... did I just say I enjoyed a pre-flight briefing?

What made a speech I've heard over 500 times so damn interesting? There are two explanations, both rooted deep in cognitive neuroscience. First, the speech was unexpected. We listen with baited anticipation to hear things that surprise us.

That's why talk show hosts and newscasters bait listeners with phrases like: "When we come back we're going to show you an amazing video of a..." and we wait to see it.

Second, it was emotional. Emotional messages (and it doesn't matter what emotion the message invokes) not only captures and keeps our attention, but it helps in the uptake and storage of that message into long term memory. That's right, you tend to remember and recall emotional messages and events with much more accuracy than boring messages and boring events. How well does it work?

That flight attendant greeting I shared with you was from a flight I took in 2005. I remember it like it was yesterday.

Ok... for you instructors out there who are sharing important, life-saving messages. Remember... make portions of your message unexpected and use emotions. Both will not only keep attention, but they will also help in learning and recall. Anyone who has attended one of my programs knows I use a healthy dose of both. The results are truly win-win. The attendees are satisfied with their day of learning of how lessons from cognitive neuroscience can improve responder safety and I have the satisfaction of knowing those lessons are going to stick with the attendees for a long time.

23-SITUATIONAL READINESS

The Situational Awareness Matters mission is dedicated to improving situational awareness of first responders. The precursor to situational awareness is situational readiness. I define situational readiness as: Having the ability to anticipate what things need to be in place to be well-prepared for an emergency response; and then, taking the steps necessary to ensure those things are done in advance of the actual response. What, precisely is needed to ensure situational readiness? Here's 10 things that make a good start to the list:

The list is in no particular order, nor can I call it complete. Rather, it's what is coming to my mind as I reflect on what I know of organizations who display strong situational readiness.

Situational Readiness List

1. Hiring of the right people for the right reasons.

2. Firing the wrong people for the right reasons.

3. Developing a comprehensive program to train supervisors how to be leaders of people.

4. Building a safety culture where egos are kept in check and self-esteem is strong.

5. Ensuring members have all the tools and equipment necessary to ensure success.

6. Ensuring members are thoroughly trained on how to use their tools and equipment.

7. Training members for success using realistic and repetitive evolutions, scenarios and simulations.

8. Ensuring the focus is first, and foremost, on the prevention of emergencies.

9. Evaluating opportunities for self-improvement following each emergency response.

10. Making small, incremental improvements over time. Avoid changing things at a pace that is faster than the organization can sustain.

Situational Non-Readiness List

Now, let's look at the antithesis list. These are the hallmarks of organizations who are not well-prepared.

1. Hiring the wrong people for the wrong reasons.

2. Keeping poor performers whose attitude and disposition drag everyone down.

3. Doing nothing to train existing or newly promoted supervisors on how to lead people.

4. Allowing the organization to be run by leaders with big egos and poor self-esteem.

5. Denying the members the tools and equipment to be successful.

6. Withholding the training on how to effectively use their tools and equipment.

7. Training in unrealistic ways. Taking shortcuts and just going through the motions or doing no training at all.

8. Focusing entirely on suppression and ignoring prevention.

9. Ignoring the lessons from mistakes made at emergencies.

10. Making no improvements or trying to make major improvements quickly so the organization is set-up for frustration and failure.

Compare the lists and decide for yourself. Does your organization have situational readiness?

24-THE FACILITATED DEBRIEF

One of the things I am thankful for in life (among many) is safe air travel. A lot of time, effort and money is spent to ensure flight crews develop and maintain strong situational awareness. The chances of getting killed in a commercial airline accident while traveling with one of the top 20 carriers is 1:87 million. That gives me comfort. But it also causes me, as a researcher and practitioner of first responder safety, to contemplate how the airlines have been able to create such an impeccable safety record. From that inquiry has come many lessons that I now share with first responders. One of those is the process of a facilitated debrief. Here's how it works:

A facilitated debrief is a very productive way to glean the lessons of a casualty or near-miss event and create a plan for self-improvement. The airlines have been using facilitated debriefs for years to improve aviation safety.

The debrief process is very different from OSHA or NIOSH investigations. The questions are different, the motives are different and the outcomes are very different. For both OSHA and NIOSH, the investigation process uses a scripted set of questions and the reports are a structured assessment of the organization based on the motives of the agency.

In a facilitated debrief the facilitator is not restricted by the rules of any federal agency to guide the inquiry. No questions or areas of the operations are off-limits and the process often uncovers many, many opportunities for self-reflection and self-improvement that would never, otherwise, have been identified.

The debrief should be conducted by public safety practitioners from outside the department who are familiar with best practices. The facilitators should possess little interest in citing chapters and versus from laws or national standards that may be devoid of real applicability to the department. OSHA and NIOSH will do enough of that. The recommendations are very organization-specific and seek to identify root causes for the incident and offers tangible solutions.

Topical areas addressed in a facilitated debrief might, for example, address (in detail): communications, teamwork, decision making, dispatch, accountability, command, training, physical fitness, SOPs/SOGs and others.

One of the best features about a facilitated debrief is the organization's administration and members can take comfort in knowing the debriefers are not investigators and the lessons are being captured for the sake of improvement, not punishment, fines or to create a list of mistakes that should not have been done.

There's no judgment in the facilitated debrief process. The facilitators are there to learn from the members who were "boots on the ground" at the incident; to obtain an intense understanding of the how and why; and, to give immediate usable advice that will improve safety.

The facilitated debrief report is issued to the department to do with as they please. It's not published and subjected to the scrutiny of others (unless, of course, the department wishes to share their lessons)... and many do.

25-DEFENSIVE DECISION MAKING

The decision to be defensive or to transition tactics from offensive to defensive at a structure fire requires strong situational awareness and it may be one of the hardest decisions a commander can make. The difficulty with this decision is not rooted in tactical shortcomings. The problem is more fundamental.

The challenge of being defensive or transitioning tactics from offensive to defensive is one of ego and self-esteem. Let's face it, firefighters do not like to lose. A great deal of time, effort and money is expended on the training and equipment to facilitate success. Training is based on successful outcomes. Advance the line into a training building and the fire is put out and the building never collapses. It works, as planned, every time.

First responders are not taught how to fail. And if failure is never an outcome, confidence rises and, subsequently, so does the ego. This is basic human psychology and it is predictable.

This can make it difficult for some commanders to be defensive from the start or to transition to defensive tactics. Defensive tactics can be thought by some to be an admission of failure. A commander who decides to be defensive from the start may hear objections from subordinates.

If a commander transitions from offensive to defensive, they are likely to also hear about it from the crews ordered to exit the structure. Why? Because the crew members self-esteem suffers as their abilities to be successful (i.e., slay the dragon) are called into question.

Coincidentally, one of the most sickening signs of low self-esteem, over inflated ego and over confidence are displayed on the "NO FEAR" decals some firefighters wear on their helmets. Personally, if I wore a decal on my helmet that portrayed how I felt when I sent firefighters into structure fires it would read "SCARED TO DEATH!"

The surest way to failure is to have fireground decisions made by overconfident commanders with large egos and low self-esteem.

When commanders start worrying more about the consequences of having a firefighter die under their command than the damage their self-esteem will sustain for making a defensive tactical decision, the number of fires that are fought from a defensive position will increase and the number of fatalities will decline.

26-CRAWL, WALK, RUN

The inspiration for this chapter comes from Situational Awareness Matters member and Fire Chief, Todd Johnson, and the members of the Woodbury Fire Department. Yesterday I was invited to observe a skills-based training evaluation that was more than a year in the making and involved over 100 practice exercises.

The crews were dispatched to a structure fire. They arrived, in a realistic staggered timeline at a 40×40 building (a parks and recreation warming house) that was full of simulated smoke. The objectives were simple: Vent, enter, search, attack. Seems simple enough. So why did they perform over 100 practices exercise to get it right?

The answer lays with the Woodbury Fire Department Training Officer Chris Klein. During officers meetings, evaluations were being held on firefighter performances at structure fires and the officers were contemplating the introduction of positive pressure ventilation as a new firefighting strategy. The command team realized there are a small number of critical success factors at a structure fire incident and these factors could be documented and firefighters could be trained for success using a list of critical tasks and repetitive training.

Crawl

The command team developed a checklist of critical tasks and used that to launch the new positive pressure ventilation training initiative. It started with handing the crews the checklist and having them walk and talk through each task in civilian clothes. This was a cognitive, hands-off exercise designed to get the crews familiar with the tasks on the list.

Walk

During subsequent drills the crews donned their gear and performed the tasks with checklists in-hand. Read the item, perform the task. Read the next item, perform the task. This was done in a repetitive fashion until the entire task list could be performed without the benefit of the checklist.

Run

Finally, the crews got to perform the tasks at realistic simulations. Initially using simulated smoke and fire and eventually at the St. Paul Training Center where they burned Class A materials. When the stress level is raised, it is expected that some items on the list may be overlooked and some "old habits" might surface. The training evolutions provided opportunities to hit the pause button and fix problems in real-time.

The underlying objective of their training was to introduce the concept of positive pressure ventilation and dynamic risk assessment (essentially knowing when to be offensive and when to be defensive).

Outcomes

On the day I observed their training, chief officers from the neighboring fire departments Fire Chief Greg Malmquist from the Lake Elmo Fire Department and Deputy Fire Chief Kevin Wold from the Oakdale Fire Department served as evaluators. The evaluators were provided with the checklists and graded the performance of crews. The performances were not flawless but the crews did perform all the critical criteria on the checklists.

Outside Evaluators

Using experienced chief officers from neighboring departments was a very smart decision for several reasons. First, internal personnel become desensitized to internal evaluators. When the evaluators are from the outside there is a heightened level of awareness about being watched and evaluated. Second, external evaluators are able to see things that internal evaluators may not see because they are so invested in their ways of doing things they cannot see their own shortcomings.

27-EMOTIONS

It is a widely held belief that the best decisions are made without the interference of emotions. Economists and statisticians alike stand fast to this belief – the best decisions are made with using pure logic. Facts and formulas lead to the most rational decisions. But do they? Image for a moment if the emotional control center of a person's brain were removed. Would that person then make better decisions? To answer that question I want to introduce you to Phineas Gage

Gage was a construction foreman for a railroad company and on September 13, 1845 he sustained an injury that made him the subject of neuro-researchers to this day.

While placing an explosive charge into a rock using a tamping rod, the ordinance accidentally detonated and the three-foot, seven inch rod went through Gage's skull.

Amazingly, Gage survived an injury that would, to this day, be fatal to many. His physical recovery was no less amazing to doctors. Within ten weeks of the injury Gage returned to work. Life was normal again. Or was it?

There was something fundamentally wrong with Gage. He suffered no memory loss and no motor skill deficits (sans the loss of his left eye and the depth perception challenges it might create from having monocular vision). But Gage was clearly "different."

His behavior had changed. In addition to a change in his personality, one of the most notable deficits was Gage could no longer make a coherent decision. The accident destroyed a portion of his brain in the prefrontal lobe that controls emotions. Gage could no longer make good decisions for the lack of emotional input into the process.

Many subsequent studies involving patients with traumatic brain injuries, lesions and tumors have validated the importance of the emotional control center in the process of decision making.

We now know that emotions are a critical component of decision making, though economists and statisticians might still choose to disagree.

Thanks to the advances in modern medicine, researchers are now able to gauge a person's emotional response to a stimulus and predict behavior long before the (apparent) rational decision is made.

One study I recall reading involved asking Chief Executive Officers to register their "gut" (emotional) solution to a problem prior to embarking on the long, often difficult and timely journey of gathering all the facts and evidence needed to make a "good" decision. When the dust settled, in a vast majority of the cases, the emotional "gut" decision equaled or was better than the rational, non-emotional decision.

The ability of the emotional brain to solve problems and influence decision making is the very concept that Malcolm Gladwell wrote about in his best-selling novel, Blink. While Gladwell is not a researcher, his writing is well-researched and, for the most part, accurately portrayed.

The take away: Emotions are essential – no critical – to making quality decisions. I do not advocate making purely emotional decisions. Rather, I'd say trust your gut, but validate it with some proof – facts and data – that confirm you're on the right track. But never dismiss your gut feelings. They're telling you something... and the message is coming right from your prefrontal cortex.

28-LEADERSHIP MEANS... LEADING!

In chapter 25 I discussed how first responders often display bravado and made the following statement:

Coincidentally, one of the most sickening signs of low self-esteem, over inflated ego and over confidence are displayed on the "NO FEAR" decals some firefighters wear on their helmets. Personally, if I wore a decal on my helmet that portrayed how I felt when I send firefighters into structure fires it would read "SCARED TO DEATH!"

I made a similar comment in a post on my social media feeds.

My Twitter feed, Facebook, LinkedIn and email lit up like a Christmas tree. I was absolutely humbled by the amount of positive comments (and, believe it or not, NO negative comments). I found that encouraging. But one piece of feedback I received, via Facebook, blew me away!

I received a very nice comment from a soon-to-be promoted Battalion Chief that read:

"Thank you for this statement. As an incident commander I feel this way every time my crews are on an interior attack. I am someone who holds you in high regard and for you to make this statement lets me know that I am not alone. Thank You!"

But it didn't end there. I sent a message back, thanking him for his kind words and his support of my mission.

Then, within a couple of days, I received another message from him. Only this one contained a picture.

Joe Lyons, a soon-to-be-promoted Battalion Chief for the Westfield (IN) Fire Department, put his ego and self-esteem on public display with a statement of raw honesty. The picture he sent was his new white fire helmet. And on the back was a decal that read: "Scared to death!" This is especially impressive coming from a company officer on the verge of being promoted to a position with direct command responsibility.

To lead is to do the right things for the right reasons without regard for judgment by others. Joe Lyons is a leader and, by my account, a hero for making a bold and honest statement that, I hope and pray, represents how EVERY incident commander feels while making the decision to send firefighters into high-risk, high-consequence environments.

Leadership means... Leading! Thank you Joe, and all the other company and command officers out there who put the safety of personnel above ego.

I often say it feels like I'm trying to push a heavy rock up a steep hill with my message and support from friends makes the task much easier... or at least more enjoyable.

29-COMPLACENCY

Curiosity killed the cat. But it's not curiosity that is killing firefighters. It's complacency contributing to flawed situational awareness. What does it mean to be complacent? I could offer you the Webster's dictionary definition. Instead, I'd like to offer you a definition based on my observations of those who suffer from the affliction.

Complacent: To believe that bad things only happen to other people; To fall into a comfortable rut of apathy – laziness; To have enjoyed success for so long as to believe all actions will result in successful outcomes; To rely on knowledge and skills that have grown stale for lack of practice and renewal; To develop a sense of indifference – to lack concern for – one's safety and well-being. Let's break this down now by expounding on each component of the definition.

To believe that bad things only happen to other people

This is often rooted in a mindset of judgment. While watching a video or reading about a casualty incident, the complacent firefighter becomes a judge. The mindset is not one of trying to understand the root cause of what happened and to extract the lesson behind the lesson. Instead, the complacent firefighter wants to ridicule and offer judgment upon the misfortunes of others. One who is judging, cannot learn. This causes the lessons to be missed and perpetuates the belief that bad things only happen to other people.

To fall into a comfortable rut of apathy – laziness

The energy required to develop and maintain competent is immense. It requires cognitive and physical effort to develop the knowledge and skills essential for top performance. Any deviation from being exceptionally prepared will result in a consequence, right? Hardly. In fact, in the vast majority of cases large deviations from top performance have no consequence.

That is both a blessing and a curse. If such deviations always resulted in casualties, the results would be catastrophic. For that, we are blessed. Yet it is the same lack of consequence that promotes apathy. The proof that one need not work as hard rests in the successful outcomes achieved despite a reduction in knowledge and skill development/maintenance.

To have enjoyed success for so long as to believeall actions will result in successful outcomes

The surest route to success is to find something that works well and do it over and over again – to perfect performance. But what is to happen if the successful outcomes are not from skill, but luck? Even when outcomes are good, there are still lessons to be learned and shared. Reviewing near-miss reports are a good way to witness, from a distance, departments who were enjoying success and then had a near-catastrophe.

To rely on knowledge and skills that havegrown stale for lack of practice and renewal

For skill and knowledge to be retained and useful, they must be practiced over and over again... and then over and over AGAIN... rinse and repeat. The process of learning and relearning skills is never ending. The pathways of the brain remain strong through repetition. Just because something was learned in recruit school 10 years ago does not mean the skillset is still flawless. Every expert in every field practices incessantly to keep skills sharp. So must firefighters.

To develop a sense of indifference –to lack concern for – one's safety and well-being

This is, perhaps, the most pathetic part of complacency as some firefighters lose sight of the fact that out there, somewhere in the world, are other people who love and depend on us. If not for yourself, fight complacency for them. I have been involved in helping several fire departments in the process of healing from a loss. It's tragic when the catastrophe could have been prevented if the members were more diligent and took the risk of their jobs more seriously.

The complacency within an organization is often a byproduct of the organization's culture, undisciplined leadership and individual member mindsets. I can change. The journey of one thousand miles begins with a single step. Do something today... take a step toward reducing complacency.

30-SAFETY TRUMPS SELF-ESTEEM

Part of the process to develop and maintain situational awareness at an emergency scene is having the ability to predict the future of the event. It's called *projection* and it's the highest level of situational awareness.

To be good at projecting the future, it is necessary to have expectations about the future events. One expectation is what will happen (outcomes) based on the tasks assigned to responders. The second expectation is – How long will it take for the first expectation to occur. At some point, someone may look at the incident and realize things are not meeting expectations. When that happens, there are only three decision options and the quality of that decision may be based more on self esteem than job knowledge.

Let's take a structure fire scenario. A crew is sent in on the attack. The commander has an expectation that black smoke is going to turn into white smoke (the victory) once the crew reaches the seat of the fire and puts the wet stuff on the red stuff.

The commander assesses the factors that help determine the time expectation for the task to be accomplished, such as:

1. Crew size and crew abilities/training;

2. Building size, construction, conditions, contents;

3. Smoke color, volume, velocity and density; and,

4. Fire color, volume, velocity and density.

Let's say, hypothetically, the commander at a residential room and contents structure fire has an expectation that the black smoke coming out a window is going to turn white in 8 minutes. At the 8-minute mark the commander should assess the progress and compare the conditions to the expectations. If the conditions meet expectations (i.e., black smoke is gone and white smoke had replaced it) then the commander can take comfort in knowing things are going to plan (VICTORY! – YEA!)

But what if things aren't going to plan (i.e., the black smoke hasn't gone away). In fact, it's got worse, not better. At that point the commander has three decision options:

Decision 1: Leave the crew inside to continue on their mission (or continue the mission with modifications).

Decision 2: Deploy additional resources.

Decision 3: Order the withdrawal of resources from the structure.

At the most fundamental level, some might think this decision entails a logical assessment of facts. In reality, the decision is as likely, if not more likely, to be based on an emotional factor – self esteem.

Yes, self esteem. First responders are action-oriented, aggressive, competitive people. It's part of what makes responders so damn good at what they do. But, it is also an Achilles heal.

When a commander orders a crew out of a building before the fire is out it is the admission of failure (LOSER – BOO!). The fire has won. The commander has lost.

Crews inside aren't going to be very happy with the order to withdraw either. In fact, in nearly every single case where commanders have told me they ordered crews out of structure fire it was met with resistance – "Give us just a few more minutes, we've almost got it." Why? Self esteem of the crew. They're very self worth is being called into question when the commander orders a withdrawal.

A Solution

Set realistic expectations about outcomes, keep track of time, and stand ready to order a withdraw if the incident is not progressing to expectations. Talk with crews, in advance of an incident about how the decision to go defensive will make everyone feel. It is important to flush these feelings out and get firefighters talking about it.

Discuss and obtain an agreement that safety trumps self-esteem in decision making. Practice the process of transitioning from offensive to defensive. It will be much easier to do it in real life if it has been practiced.

Discussion

1. How does it make you feel to transition tactics from offensive to defensive?

2. Have you discussed the importance of safety over self-esteem in decision making with your crew?

3. Have you practiced the skills of transitioning tactics from offensive to defensive?

31-DISCIPLINE WILL NOT IMPROVE SAFETY

I read with great interest (and concern) an article recently published about how the San Francisco Fire Department is being fined $21,000 by state investigators for violations to safety laws that led to the deaths of two firefighters on June 2. My concern for this action is not an attempt, in any way, to diminish the tragic loss of two firefighters that, by the article's account, could have been avoided.

My concern has to do with the message punitive action sends for behaviors that have likely been occurring in their fire department for many, many years. Issues of situational awareness rarely occur for the first time at a casualty incident. On this fateful day, enough of the department's persistent shortcomings aligned concurrently to flaw situational awareness, contribute to poor decision making and resulted in a tragedy. To levy a fine on the department is not likely to impact the needed behavior change because the financial penalties do not address the root problem.

Here's what I wish they would have done...

It is my hope (ok... call it a wish) that fire departments who suffer catastrophic outcomes would undergo a thorough facilitated debriefing to help the department's leaders understand not only the root cause of the problem, but how to fix it. Paying out cash to a state agency isn't going to improve anyone's understanding about what happened and it's surely not going to fix the root cause of the problem. In fact, I'd bet dollars to donuts the state agency that levied the fine doesn't have a clue about root cause analysis and how to fix the problems. They're not in the fix-the-problem business. They're in the penalize-for-errors business. Trust me... it's the wrong approach to improve safety.

In aviation, they stopped using a punishment system and started rewarding employees for reporting their near-misses and mishaps. You did not read that wrong. Self-reporting a near-miss or a mishap through the Aviation Safety Reporting System (ASRS) results in a reward – immunity from discipline. That is a game changer.

A culture of safety

The concept of getting away from discipline as a way to change behavior was talked about extensively in Sydney Dekker's book, Just Culture. (By the way... Just Culture is the book Chesley Sullenburger was reading in the days leading up to the incident where he landed his Airbus 330 in the Hudson River (with zero casualties, I might add). Ok... back to the lesson. A *'Just' Culture* is one where employees are not fearful of the consequences of making mistakes that are the result of human error. Absent fear, lessons are shared, root causes are identified and real fixes can be put into place.

Does a Just Culture work?

Does a Just Culture work? You be the judge. If you fly on one of the top twenty commercial airlines your chances of dying in an aviation accident is about 1:85 million. Those are damn good odds. For you Six Sigma zealots, that's a Six Sigma safety record! If you don't know what I'm talking about, look it up... or trust me. It mean's they have safety figured out.

Punishment Damages Learning

An organization, or for that matter, an entire profession (like ours) cannot learn while operating in an environment of fear for consequences. It leads to hiding valuable information that might otherwise be part of the solution. Our mistakes not only need to be learned, but they need to be assimilated and commonality among them identified. The closest thing we have to a system like the ASRS is the Firefighter Near-Miss Reporting System (NMRS).

NMRS Strengths and Opportunities

The Near-Miss Reporting System is a step in the right direction. It provides an opportunity for fire service safety lessons to be shared through a searchable database. However, the NMRS is never going to achieve what the ASRS has accomplished so long as those making the mistakes suffer consequences, regardless of how well-intended the firefighters or fire commanders were. Consequence creates fear and fear prohibits the sharing of information.

Additionally, no one is completing a thorough analysis of Near-Miss data. I've asked for that to be done. Hell, I've even offered to do it myself. Thus far, I have not been granted access to contact the near-miss reporters. Absent the opportunity to interview the participants, it is impossible to extract accurate data to determine the root cause. I understand the need to protect the identities of reporters of near-miss data. However, I've been told, first hand, there are lots of near-miss reporters out there who'd love to share their lessons. I am fortunate to be able to meet many of them in my classes and I frequently take the opportunity to interview them.

How Could We Improve?

How could we improve? I'm glad you asked. When you read a casualty or a near-miss report that sites flawed situational awareness as a contributing factor, you might as well use the report paper to wipe your backside. It's meaningless.

I've uncovered and studied over 100 barriers to situational awareness (Incidentally, I address the top 50 barriers to situational awareness in my program Fifty Ways to Kill a First Responder). Simply implicating situational awareness accomplishes nothing. We have to understand the root cause of the problem to be able to fix it.

A Solution

This is going to perhaps be the boldest statement I'll make in this book. But it's something I say often in my live presentations. We MUST STOP punishing our employees/members for the consequences that result when well-intended people make errors. We need to learn from these errors, and stop judging and punishing. The person who makes an error in decision making that results in the death of a firefighter is suffering a great loss as well. Trust me. I get the opportunity to work with departments who've had line of duty deaths. They're suffering.

The first step in the healing and learning process is to acknowledge humans are fallible creatures, especially under stress. Yes, much can be done to improve performance under stress in advance of an emergency but most departments don't train for that. Not because they don't want to. Rather because they don't know how to. Training to improve performance under stress requires having a deep knowledge of how the brain and body change physically, chemically and emotionally. Firefighters and training officers don't know this stuff. They give me that feedback after every program I deliver.

Discussion

1. Should well-intended firefighters, company officers or commanders be punished for making bad decisions that result in a casualty event?

2. How does your department learn from mistakes?

3. Do your members blow the whistle on themselves and self-report their mistakes without fear of retribution?

32-YOUR WEAKEST LINK

It has often been said: *'A chain is only as strong as its weakest link.'* This is true. Regardless of how fortified the individual links are, when the chain is stressed under a load, the breaking point will be the weakest link. The same can be said of situational awareness at an emergency scene. Each member of the team is a link in the proverbial chain. The *load* at an emergency incident is workload and stress (physical and emotional). When situational awareness breaks down, the entire team is vulnerable.

I make this point because the audiences in my situational awareness and decision making classes are often senior staff and company officers – the decision makers and commanders. For whatever reason, the line personnel are often left out (maybe it's a financial constraint – I'm not judging, just observing). Ironically, when the program is over I often receive feedback that includes: *'Everyone on our department needs to be trained on this material.'*

Indeed! The emergency scene can become a very frustrating, not to mention extremely dangerous, place if any responder is operating with under-developed situational awareness. The high stress, time constrained incident scene is no place to teach situational awareness. But it is the place where flawed situational awareness contributes to bad outcomes.

The fundamentals of situational awareness, decision making (and the human behavior that contributes to success and failure) are best taught in a calm, low stress classroom environment. This includes *EVERYONE!* Not just commanders and officers. If the newest firefighter operating at an emergency scene has flawed situational awareness, it can jeopardize scene safety.

Developing the situational awareness of the newest responders can be especially challenging because they have so much to learn. It pains me to talk to young responders and ask them about their training. They tell me about how they have been trained as firefighters, rescue technicians, haz-mat specialists, EMTs and paramedics.

When I ask them about their training on situational awareness and decision making you can hear the crickets in the room. A responder who lacks understanding about how to develop and maintain situational awareness is a weak link.

A Solution

The solution to this problem, while simple, may not be easy. Simply, all responders need to be trained on how to develop and maintain strong situational awareness. What keeps this from being easy is those people who would be the teachers of this topic do not understand enough about the topic to be a good teacher. Situational awareness is much more than paying attention. It takes me two full days to comprehensively teach a class on situational awareness and decision making. TWO DAYS!

My situational awareness and decision making classes do not focus on strategy and tactics. In fact, I never talk once about tactical performance. There are plenty of other people out there on a local level who are good tactical instructors who can teach that.

Teaching situational awareness and decision making is a specialty topic. Make sure ALL your responders are being properly taught about situational awareness from an instructor who possesses a deep understanding of how to develop and maintain situational awareness, how it can erode, and how it can be regained if it does erode.

Discussion

1. Share your understanding of how situational awareness is develop, maintained, eroded and regained.

2. Describe the training you received on how to develop and maintain situational awareness.

3. Discuss how you identify your weak links as it relates to situational awareness and the process your department uses to fix this challenge.

33-STOP JUDGING

Oftentimes when I am talking with first responders about the role of situational awareness and casualty incidents, especially the ones that have recently occurred, they share with me their opinions and frustrations about the performance of the responders and the decisions made by command staff. If I have learned anything, it's first responders are opinionated and, in general, are not very understanding or forgiving when assessing errors.

Stated another way, first responder are quick to judge and slow to learn. I used to be this way. Earlier in my career I would ask: *Why were they doing that?* Now, I ask, *Why did that make sense to be doing what they were doing at that moment in time?* Asking the latter question opens my mind up to learning. You see, I can offer all kinds of opinions as to why I think the responders were doing what they were doing. But I cannot possibly know the answer to the latter question without asking the people directly involved.

This is exactly what I do when I conduct facilitated debriefs for departments who have had a significant near-miss or a casualty event. It is critical to learn everything possible about why casualty events occur so the lessons can improve the safety of all responders.

A Solution

When responders stop judging and start learning, situational awareness will improve. Borrowing from Steven Covey's Seven Habits of Highly Effective People, *seek first to understand, then to be understood.* Stop judging the performance of others and start understanding why the actions and decisions being made at the time of the casualty event made sense to the responders.

Discussion

1. What process does your department use to learn from your near-miss and casualty incidents?

2. What process do you use to learn from the near-miss and casualty incidents of other departments?

3. Has your department every conducted a facilitated debrief conducted by an independent facilitator?

34-SIZE-UP

Situational awareness starts with capturing clues and cues in your environment (perception) and then understanding what those clues and cues mean (comprehension). At a structure fire the process of capturing information should involve a complete 360-degree size-up of the scene. Many departments have policies that stipulate the completion of a 360-degree size-up. Yet, for some reason, it's not always done. This chapter provides an explanation why that might happen and how to fix the problem.

I have previously written about how training sets up firefighters for success or failure. I speak to this phenomenon frequently in my safety program. Here's an example of how first responders might be trained for failure as it relates to size-ups.

While conducting a structure fire training scenario an instructor has two options for how to train firefighters about conducting a 360-degree size-up.

The instructor can simply talk about completing a 360-degree size-up. If this approach is taken, the firefighters will nod their heads as a sign of understanding. Some may even become frustrated because the instructor is "talking down" to the firefighters by stating the obvious.

Alternatively, the instructor might require the firefighters to physically complete the 360-degree size-up by walking around the structure. Again, firefighters may become frustrated because it seems like a waste of time to walk around a structure the firefighters know so well.

Under stress, humans perform based on habits developed through repetition. Further, stress can impact the brain's ability to comprehensively recall verbal instructions. This has been tested many times in research studies and I suspect it has played out many times at fire scenes as well. And most importantly, muscles do not learn from verbal instructions. Muscles learn from muscle movement. If the muscles aren't moving in training, they aren't learning.

A Solution

Train firefighters for success by having them physically perform 360-degree size-ups at every training scenario. However, in order to build "Team Situational Awareness" I propose instructors add a second component to completing the size-up – communicating the size-up has been completed and a radio report of what was observed. As noted in previous chapters, even the absence of clues and cues is important information to be shared to build situational awareness. The person who completes the size-up should provide a radio report that starts with *"Upon completion of the 360-degree size-up...* (and complete the report)." As important as completing the size-up is training on what to look for and what to report.

Here are some action items to improve situational awareness:

1. Ensure there is a policy that requires 360-degree size-ups.

2. Ensure 360-degree size-ups are built into training evolutions... every time.

3. Train firefighters on what to look for during the size-up (present AND absent clues).

4. When a company officer completes a 360-degree size-up, have it announced over the radio: "Upon completion of the 360-degree size-up, we have..."

Discussion

1. Does your first arriving officer always complete a 360-degree size-up? If the answer is yes, how do you know it was done?

2. What clues and cues (both present and absent) would you look for while completing a 360-degree size-up to help you form a strong situational awareness about what is happening?

3. What clues and cues (both present and absent) might indicate the fire should be defensive versus offensive attack?

35-SIZE-UP PRIORITIES

During my open conference call last Friday to discuss situational awareness challenges and opportunities (which, by the way... was really enjoyable) I had a chief officer from Wisconsin (thanks Lance) ask a question about company officer priorities on sizing up a residential dwelling fire. It's a question I get asked often and have built the answer into the ten best practices I share at the end of the Fifty Ways to Kill a First Responder program. So, if you have attended that program, this will be a nice refresher for you. If you haven't, then consider using this list to help in your initial size-up.

First, before I jump into the list, I want to share a little B.S. with you... *Brain Science*. Program attendees know that I rarely make recommendations about why responders should do something a certain way without some tie-in to the neuroscience that supports my claims. I wish more instructors would do the same. We'd have less anecdotal tales being told and more lessons being taught that are backed by research.

Here's the 4-1-1 on the B.S.: The human brain can take in, process, comprehend and recall a very limited amount of unrelated information. Complicating this is the vulnerability of the short-term memory (also known as working memory) to quickly forget. Quickly being defined as: *Within seconds.* As a side note, the stability of short-term memory can be improved by repetition and it tends to hold on to things that are emotional.

So, how many pieces of unrelated information can the average human's short-term memory handle? About seven (give or take two). That's not very many pieces of information considering how complex emergency scenes can be. And, to complicate matters, stress can reduce that number to five (give or take two). This point becomes ridiculously important to understanding our limitations as humans... and commanders.

First-arriving officers, under stress, can process about five pieces of information coherently. And, as you know, there may be dozens (maybe even hundreds) of pieces of information coming your way. Some are critical. Many are not.

The trick, if there is a trick, is to identify, in advance, those pieces of information that are most important. Seek them out, and use them as the foundation for good decision making.

For example, at a structure fire, the *short list* of critical clues and cues might include:

Smoke and fire conditions: What is the color, volume, velocity and density of the smoke and fire. And, of course, understanding what that means in relation to what is burning, where it is burning, how hot it's burning and where it is traveling to.

The building construction and decomposition: What is the building made out of and where is the building at in the process of falling down? Make no mistake about it, a building on fire is in the process of falling down. The forces of gravity are in play and when the building weakens enough, gravity will win and the building will fall down. To understand this risk is to understand building construction and building decomposition.

Risk-benefit assessment: Are there savable lives in the structure. Too often the casualty of structure fires are firefighters engaged in the act of searching a vacant structure or one where there are no savable lives. Firefighters are sworn to protect lives and property but not all lives and property can be saved. It's just a fact.

Assessing resource needs and abilities: Are there enough resources assembled to perform the tasks needed to overwhelm the fire? To determine this requires an understanding of the physics of fire and water (knowing how much water it takes to put out a certain volume of fire) and it takes knowing something about the abilities of the personnel assembled to perform the tasks. Not all crews are created equal and to fight all fires as if all crews are high quality, "A-team" performers is unrealistic.

A Solution

Ensure your size up includes these four things.

1. Smoke and fire assessment
2. Building construction and decomposition assessment
3. Risk-benefit assessment
4. Resource assessment

Discussion

1. What is the most challenging part of the size-up process for you?

2. Do you ever find yourself being overwhelmed with information? What can you do to resolve this?

3. Have you ever overlooked an important piece of information, but were so overwhelmed that you didn't realize it at the time?

36-A "MINOR" MAYDAY

Is there such a thing? A "Minor" Mayday. A crew operating in an IDLH environment suddenly finds themselves in a tough spot because _____ (you insert the reason). The crew leader's situational awareness is, at least, at that moment, strong as he immediately realizes the potential gravity of the situation and calls a Mayday. Command acknowledges the Mayday and the rapid intervention team (RIT) is called into action. But before the RIT fully deploys, something unexpected happens.

The Mayday is cancelled by the crew that called it. The cancelation is followed with "We're ok. Disregard the Mayday." The RIT stands down and everything returns to normal. The officer who called the Mayday feels embarrassed because the situation so quickly rectified and what appeared to be an issue of significant potential consequence turned out to be non-event.

How this fire department handles the debriefing, assuming they even hold one, is of vital importance to the self-esteem of the person who called the Mayday and to the confidence others may someday have to call a Mayday when they find themselves in a tight spot.

Some critics on the department will question whether the event even qualified as a Mayday. Other critics will question whether the member overreacted by calling the Mayday in the first place. Some may even call into question the department's training practices and how the training on Mayday operations has resulted in firefighters being over zealous to call Maydays unnecessarily. (On a side note... I cannot tell you why, but some firefighters look for fault and blame like they're going to get a reward when they find it).

The firefighter who transmitted the Mayday made the right call. If a crew feels their wellbeing is in jeopardy, a quick assessment and a rapid Mayday transmission ensures the activation of help, hopefully through an adequately staffed and adequately trained rapid intervention team. The reason for the Mayday should be explored through a post incident evaluation and the entire organization should benefit from the lessons.

About a year ago I had an opportunity to talk with a fire chief who had a firefighter fall through a floor and called a Mayday. The firefighter was quickly located by other firefighters who were working in the basement and he was taken outside. His injuries were very minor and the chief downplayed the event as a non-event, almost appearing embarrassed that his department had a Mayday called in the first place. Further inquiry revealed little was done to extract and share the lessons from the event and it seemed as though the firefighter who called the Mayday was admonished for being on the spongy floor and falling through in the first place.

A Solution

Getting a firefighter beyond the fear and embarrassment of calling a Mayday is a significant hurdle that departments must acknowledge and overcome. This problem can be compounded when firefighters convince themselves the problem isn't that bad and they can work through it without having to call a Mayday.

If the problem continues to worsen (and sometimes it worsens quickly) the situation may rapidly escalate to the point where the rapid intervention team's success will be challenged. Once the window of survivability closes (something I talk about during every Mental Management of Emergencies program), no amount of resources are going to be able to change the outcome and there will be a firefighter fatality.

It is very important for departments to:

1. Develop a comprehensive Mayday and rapid intervention policy.

2. Train all firefighters, officers and commanders on how and when to call a Mayday and what everyone's role will be during a Mayday.

3. Practice calling Maydays over the radio, preferably while having the firefighters in a simulated high-stress situation.

4. Discuss scenarios where Maydays would be appropriate and how much time a firefighter should let pass before calling a Mayday.

5. Discuss how fellow firefighters should react to a "Minor" Mayday that resolves quickly (Hint: With praise and acknowledgement for the right decision made).

Discussion

1. Does your department have a comprehensive Mayday and rapid intervention policy?

2. Are your members well-trained and well-practiced for what to do during a Mayday?

3. Have you ever had a "Minor" Mayday? And if so, how did the members not directly involved in it react?

4. Have you ever had a scenario where a Mayday should have been called but, for whatever reason, was not called or was delayed?

37-BE ASSERTIVE

You're a firefighter assigned to a roof job. It's a flat metal roof and there's a lot of water on it. (Set aside for a moment all your judgment about why you're on the roof in the first place). Your situational awareness is strong and you're getting a gut felling that's causing you concern for your safety. And... you can see the same concern in the eyes of your fellow firefighters. But no one's speaking up. No one wants to be called disparaging names (as it was described to me by the firefighter who reached out to me for advice). I understand this is a tough position to be in. Your gut (intuition) is telling you get off the roof, but your pride is telling you to stay and be brave. What do you do?

This may be the toughest position a firefighter can find him or herself in. Having a gut feeling that a situation is bad and not knowing how to express those concerns to ranking officers.

In this situation, the command officer is (hopefully) on the ground and unable to see the conditions on the roof. This puts the firefighter in a position of distinct advantage to be able to see things in a way the commander cannot. So how does the firefighter let the commander know he's concerned for his wellbeing without sounding like a coward?

A lesson from aviation

The answer to this question comes from a process used in aviation. It's called the *Five Step Assertive Statement Process*. It came about because first officers were afraid to speak up to captains who, at the time, were known to have large egos and did not accept advice or criticism very well. Prior to the implementation of Cockpit Resource Management (the precursor to Crew Resource Management), the Captain was King. What the Captain said was the Gospel. No one ever dared disagree with the Captain or they would be reprimanded and admonished in front of everyone.

The only problem was, there were plenty of instances where the Captain was wrong. Captains were making mistakes and, in some instances, flying perfectly good airplanes into the ground and the first officers were saying nothing to stop it from happening. To help fix the problem, the aviation industry implemented Cockpit Resource Management as a way to get the flight crew to work better together. Know this – the Captains did not embrace the concept. Many dubbed it *'Charm School'* and opposed the notion that a first officer could actually tell a Captain he or she was making a mistake.

The Five Step Assertive Statement Process

But, the program prevailed despite all the kicking and fussing from the Captains. One of the outcomes was the Five Step Assertive Statement Process. It's a pre-established, well-communicated process for how concerns are supposed to be articulated in an aircraft.

The steps include:

1. Address the person by formal title

2. State: "I have a concern." (This is important and I'll explain why in a moment).

3. Provide details of the concern.

4. State an alternate course of action.

5. Seek the approval to implement the alternate course of action.

In action, it might sound something like this:

"Captain, I have a concern. This is a metal roof with metal trusses under it. There are thousands of pounds of water accumulating up here and this building is under stress. I would like to recommend we remove all personnel from the roof until we can find a way to relieve the water and reduce the weight. Are you ok with that?"

I have a concern

The statement – *I have a concern* – is not a casual statement. Rather, it is a *'trigger statement.'* The use of those four words, by policy, requires that the captain acknowledge and consider the concerns of the crew member. In aviation, failure to do so may lead to the captain being relieved from commanding the aircraft. This trigger statement is taught to all members of a flight crew and any member of the crew can express their concerns using it. Here's the catch: They all know it in advance. Everyone's been trained on it and they all know what it means and what they have to do when it is stated.

A Solution

Every fire department should have in place a policy that establishes a *Five Step Assertive Statement Process*. Then, when anyone on an emergency scene says to someone in authority *'I have a concern'* it is a trigger statement that requires the concern be given consideration.

Obviously, training on the process and training for how to make the statement and how to receive the statement is critical. Absent the training, a firefighter will not know how to state a concern and will be fearful if one is stated. Likewise, a commander is not likely to be accepting of a statement of concern unless the commander understands and accepts it as part of a formal process that is intended to look out for everyone's safety. A commander who cannot accept the *'I have a concern'* statement does not have a healthy ego and has a low self esteem and should not be in a position to lead firefighters into battle.

Discussion

1. Have you ever been in a position where you were concerned for your safety but did not speak up because you were afraid to or did not know how to?

2. Have you ever brought safety concerns to the attention of a supervisor at an emergency scene and been admonished for doing so? If you have, why do you think the supervisor would act that way?

3. Does your department have a formal process in place that uses a *'trigger statement'* to express safety concerns?

38-RISK VERSUS REWARD

At 2:04 am the fire department was dispatched for a fire in a commercial building. Upon arrival the first engine reports a working fire and commences with interior fire attack. Upon entry, the engine crew reports high heat conditions and low visibility, but they pressed onward. Situational awareness is marginal. Soon the second engine and first truck arrives and are pressed into action.

A second line is pulled and the truck commences with rooftop ventilation. The fire conditions worsens and a second alarm is called. Additional resources are deployed with additional hose lines. Despite the tenuous conditions, the firefighters remained true to their sworn calling, fight the dragon, and valiantly declare victory. The fire is out and no one is killed, despite several close calls. Been there? Seen that? What is to result of this heroic endeavor?

Some two years later... a vacant lot is all that remains. The firefighters can count their blessings. No injuries and no fatalities, despite several close calls. Looking back at their efforts and the risk they took to "save" a building which would only be torn down within a month of the fire, one might wonder if the *risk* justified the *reward*. Hell, I wonder if the risk versus reward notion was even on their mind as they stretched their hose lines down those high-heat, no visibility hallways. I wonder if anyone thought:

What the hell are we doing here?

What are we trying to accomplish that is worth the possibility of my children being orphaned?

If I die in this building tonight, will it have been worth it?

A Solution

Every incident should be viewed from a perspective of risk versus reward. If you cannot bring yourself off the high perch of self-emulation (one where it is thought that dying for the namesake of being a firefighter is a noble way to die), then think about those you will leave behind.

If a firefighter had died fighting the fire in the building pictured above, what would his or her widow say to their children as they stood on that street corner looking at that vacant lot, holding hands, tears rolling down their cheeks wishing for their loved one back.

NOTE: I realize this chapter may be controversial and may not be enjoyable to read. It calls into question the logic some firefighters apply toward justifying risk taking. When I was on the line I never was much in favor of being an *'outstanding'* firefighter (i.e., being one to *stand outside* a burning building).

However, with age comes wisdom and as I look back on my life as a firefighter I now realize I took a hell of a lot of risk where the reward was not worth it.

I was lucky enough to come home to my family every time. And I mean it... I was LUCKY! And for my efforts, there are still some vacant lots... 25 years later. Thanks be to God that I am here to rant about it.

Discussion

1. Does your fire department train on the concept of risk versus reward?

2. Have you ever found yourself in a high-risk situation where the reward did not justify the risk?

3. Have you ever risked your life to "save" a structure that was subsequently torn down? If so, how did that make you feel?

39-CONTEXT DEPENDENT LEARNING

As public safety providers we could make a
fundamental improvement in developing situational
awareness by looking at how we train responders.
There are some valuable lessons from brain science
that can help you improve the design of your program.
One is called *context dependent learning*. It has been
validated through numerous studies and I was
actually introduced to it by a professor in my graduate
school psychology class. If you are a training officer,
this chapter may cause you to rethink how to train
your members.

The concept of *context dependent learning* is
fundamentally simple, yet often overlooked in the
training of first responders. Essentially, it means if we
train responders in the same environment in which
they are going to perform their work they are far more
likely to recall their lessons when put back into the
same environment on the job.

As I stated earlier, I was first introduced to this in graduate school when my professor challenged the students to study for the final exam in the classroom where we would take the test. He stated he'd make sure the room was unlocked all weekend so any of us could come there to study.

As it was an executive MBA program everyone was working professionals and no one resided on campus. This meant it might be inconvenient, maybe even difficult, for students to come to the classroom to study. I took him up on his challenge though and spent an entire Saturday in that classroom studying my notes and preparing for this challenging final exam.

By golly, it worked! I got 100% on the final exam and accolades from the professor in front of the entire class. He asked me to share my secret for preparing because he'd never had anyone earn a perfect score on one of his final exams. You could have seen the jaws drop when I said I came to the classroom to study for the final. The professor donned a wide smile. Context dependent learning was validated.

A more formal research study involved two groups of SCUBA divers. One was the test group and one was the control group. The researchers put the test group in ten feet of water and gave them some information to memorize. They did the same thing with the control group, except the control group was on land. Then the researchers tested the participants by putting both groups in ten feet of water and asked them to answer questions about what they had learned.

The group that learned the information while in the water did remarkably better in recalling the information than the group that learned the information while standing on dry land. This, is *context dependent learning*. It can work in SCUBA and it can work in firefighting. If we train firefighter how to perform hands-on tasks while in a classroom, they are likely to recall less of what they learned.

A Solution

Train responders in the environment in which they will be performing their tasks. It may seem trivial, but science suggests the brain ties the lessons to the environment.
The more the learning environment mimics the working environment, the stronger the lessons are encoded into memory.

I recall learning so many of my fire, rescue, and EMS lessons either in a classroom or an apparatus bay. It wasn't very realistic, that's for sure. Now I am most critical of incident command courses that are conducted in classrooms because the environment is not context dependent. To improve recall, put commanders in their natural working environment and teach them how to command. The lessons will be more readily recalled when needed most.

Discussion

1. When you were trained in your basic fire or EMS skills, did your learning environment always mimic the real-world environment you would operate in?

2. Provide some examples where instructors taught basic skills in a context dependent environment that you would consider unique.

3. Share some ideas for how your training programs could be improved by using context dependent learning.

40-IT'S JUST A CAR FIRE

I'd like to thank one of the loyal Situational Awareness Matters readers (whose name and department I am holding in confidence) for sending me a picture and a story about a van fire, no, a *routine van fire* his department had recently. On the arrival of the engine the officer reported a working fire and the crew pulled a line and started the attack. Then, something unexpected happened, followed by something very unexpected, followed by something that was nearly tragic.

Everything seems in order. A firefighter is on the attack line in full PPE. And then, unexpectedly, the vehicle starts rolling. Before they know it, the vehicle is careening down the hill with the firefighter on the hose line in pursuit. And, to complicate the situation further, there is a firefighter in the driver's seat of the van.

How did this happen?

The crew arrived and began fighting the fire. As the vehicle started to slowly drift, one of the firefighters jumped behind the wheel to ensure the vehicle was in park. The van started rolling faster down the hill. The firefighter depressed the brake peddle. The sudden stoppage of the van caused the fire-weakened fuel line to rupture and the vehicle erupted into flames.

The firefighter was able to bail out of the vehicle before it rolled all the way to the bottom of the hill, out of reach of the attack line, and ran into two additional vehicles (one occupied). This kept the burning van from crashing into the house at the bottom of the hill.

The firefighter suffered significant burns on his face and neck because he was not wearing his Nomex hood. It was reported to me that this firefighter was in the habit of not routinely wearing his Nomex hood while fighting vehicle fires. (It has also been reported that this incident has changed his outlook on that practice).

The writer shared the following lessons with me:

1.   Nomex hoods 100% of the time.

2.   Chock the wheels at vehicle fires.

3.   Park the fire apparatus up hill and past the burning vehicle.

A Solution

Avoid falling into the trap of complacent practices that may compromise safety simply because it's something that's been done over and over again without a consequence. There is no such thing as a routine fire of any kind. Unexpected things happen and conditions can become bad quickly. Wear full protective gear. When you critique incidents, play a 'what if' game and talk through some uncommon scenarios that could have happened and how they might be handled.

Discussion

1. Do you always wear your full protective ensemble for vehicle fires?

2. Do you always chock the wheels of a vehicle on fire?

3. During incident critiques, do you routinely discuss the realistic 'what if' scenarios that did not occur (but could have) and the best way to handle it?

41-A FAIR QUESTION

I had the opportunity today to talk with a very progressive fire chief about situational awareness. I really enjoyed my conversations with him because I always learn something. He was telling me that his department just hired 17 new paid-on-call members. He shared with me that during the hiring process he visits the home of each firefighter candidate to talk with their families about the commitments and obligations of being a firefighter and the required support the firefighter will need from family members.

That's a great best practice for ensuring the family members are welcomed into their new fire department family. During one of his visits, he asked the wife of a firefighter candidate if she had any questions. By his own admission, she caught him off-guard when she asked...

"What safeguards do you have in place to ensure my husband will come home after every call?"

It's a fair question. In fact, that question is probably on the minds of every first responder's family members. Moms, dads, spouses, children, girlfriends or boyfriends, brothers or sisters... they all want to be assured the fire department is going to take care of the person who is very important in their lives.

It's a dangerous business and it's important to acknowledge that. Giving false hope that their loved one will never be in harm's way is neither fair nor accurate. The stressful working conditions of emergency responders is dangerous and can result in heart attacks and strokes (#1 killer of firefighters). Responding to and returning from an emergency call also carries an element of danger (#2 killer of firefighters). Emergency scenes are hostile environments and conditions can change quickly and unexpectedly which can result in casualties (#3 killer of firefighters). That level of brutal honesty may not endear you to the family member and it doesn't answer their question about the safeguards.

Do you have safeguards? Are they adequate? Maybe it's time to take inventory and turn that brutal honesty back on yourself. Is safety a priority or lip service in your department?

On a side note... I once rode along with a fire department where at the start of the shift a large group of firefighters were ranting about how the city had cut the fire department's health and wellness budget (and the firefighters were getting their free fitness center passes cut). *'The city doesn't give a crap about our safety'* was the theme of the rant.

Then, a call came in. I got on the apparatus and watched the four firefighters ride to the call without wearing seat belts. In fact, they all looked at me like I was from outer space when I put my seat belt on. As we rode to the call I thought to myself... *If we get in an accident and, God forbid, one of you get killed, there's going to be someone at home very upset when they learn you were not wearing a seat belt* – the low hanging fruit on the safety tree.

A Solution

Every fire department should have safeguards in place to ensure the well-being of members (with an acknowledgement that even with safeguards in place bad things can happen). Here are a few that come to mind:

1. A safety culture that lends support to members who do their jobs safely.

2. A comprehensive health and wellness program that supports member fitness to perform the strenuous tasks without consequence.

3. A thorough driver's training program that promotes safe and defensive driving, both in emergency and non-emergency modes.

4. A priority on training, both initial training and on-going training. Firefighters need to be taught how to safely perform their jobs and then be required to practice those skills routinely to ensure skill competency.

5. Well-maintained equipment and gear to safely perform the job.

6. A way to speak up when there is a concern for safety without fear of consequence.

7. A process to learn from mistakes without blame.

8. Strong leaders with healthy egos and strong self-esteems who stand up and do the right thing regardless of criticism.

9. All members with a mindset that welcomes areas for how to improve the safety of the organization and their personal safety.

I'm sure you may be able to think of a few more to add to the list.

Discussion

1. If someone who cared for you asked "*What safeguards does the department have in place to ensure you're coming home after every call?*" are you prepared to give them an answer that assures them safety is a priority?

2. Have you ever engaged your loved ones in a conversation about what concerns they have about your serving as a first responder?

3. What are some best practices you can suggest for ensuring the safety of first responders?

42 - EXPLAINING UNSAFE ACTIONS

I recently had a situational awareness conversation with a firefighter who shared the details of an incident that made him both proud and disappointed. His company officer decided to do an exterior attack at a residential dwelling fire because the conditions had deteriorated to the point where an interior attack would not be warranted.

This decision was made even though neighbors were reporting there might be someone inside. Based on what I was told, the officer made the right call. As it turns out, no one was inside and if they were the conditions were not compatible with life. This made the firefighter proud. But what happened next left him terribly disappointed.

Apparently, the officer on the second-in engine did not share the same assessment of the conditions and had his crew pull a line and initiated an interior attack. That crew made no progress on putting the fire out or conducing anything close to an effective search.

Within thirty seconds of entry they were "bailing out" of the house. The bailout crew commented about how quickly conditions deteriorated around them. These comments left the defensive crew absolutely stunned. The exterior crew saw the conditions as being untenable well before the aggressive crew even entered the structure.

The firefighter I interviewed described the interior crew as "hot dogs" who are always pushing the envelope of safety to the very limits and this time had a consequence as two members on the hot dog crew got burned... needlessly. So why did they enter an environment they should not have been in to begin with? Here are ten possible explanations to ponder:

1. The officer on the interior crew suffers from low self-esteem and felt he had to justify his value to the organization and his fellow crew members by being overly aggressive.

2. The officer on the interior crew has an over inflated ego and is of the mindset that "real" firefighters "always" conduct interior attacks, regardless of conditions.

3. The officer on the interior crew arrived with a predisposed action in his mind (aggressive offensive). With that mindset, no amount of clues or cues indicating that's a poor action choice is going to change his mind.

4. The officer on the interior crew suffered tunnel vision and did not complete a size-up that included the development of strong situational awareness.

5. The other members on the interior crew were too afraid of the officer to speak up, even if they felt an aggressive interior attack was not appropriate.

6. The other members on the interior crew did not know how to speak up to express their concerns to a superior officer.

7. The officer on the interior crew has developed a habit of "always" conducting an aggressive interior attack. Habits are hard to break.

8. The officer on the interior crew suffers from the "duty to die" syndrome and believes that it his "sworn duty" to be in those conditions and if he dies while doing his job, that is a noble way to die.

9. The officer on the interior crew has fought many interior fires that he believes were as bad as this one, or worse, and it always turned out ok (no injuries).

10. The officer on the defensive crew – who was the first arriving officer and designated incident commander – did not stand up to the rogue officer and forbid the interior attack. He stood by and let it happen. He lacked a strong command presence.

There you have it. Ten possible explanations for unsafe actions that resulted in two senseless firefighter injuries.

A Solution

When you have an event similar to the one described above it is important to learn from the event. Oftentimes nothing is said. Sometimes the aggressive interior crew is lauded for their heroic actions. That results in positive reinforcement for undesirable behaviors. Sometimes the crew who chooses to be defensive may be admonished for not being aggressive enough. That results in negative reinforcement of desired behaviors.

While these are ten possible explanations, without being at the scene or knowing any of the members of the department who were there, it is virtually impossible for me to know for sure why this happened. But the tough questions need to be asked and the core issue for unsafe behaviors needs to be addressed. NOTE: The sad part of this story is the officer who made the decision to conduct an aggressive interior attack was not among the injured firefighters.

Discussion

1. Have you ever been in a situation where your officer made a decision to be aggressive offensive under conditions that were untenable? How did you handle it?

2. Why do you think it made sense to the interior officer to conduct aggressive interior operations under such deteriorating conditions?

3. What are your thoughts about the strength of the situational awareness of the two officers? Why was there such a difference?

4. What can you do to reduce the possibility that you'll ever be in this situation?

43-ASSUMING OR CREATING RISK

I recently read an article where the author was taking exception to the risk management maxim: *'We will risk a lot to save a lot and risk little to save little.'* There are several variations on this maxim, including: *'Great risks will be taken to save savable lives; Moderate risks will be taken to save savable property; and, No risk will be taken to save what is unsavable.'*

Risk management is an essential component to the development and maintenance of strong situational awareness. The premise of the author was firefighting is, by its nature, risky and no catchy phrase is going to make it safer. I agree. In fact, I wholeheartedly agree. But there is fundamentally a huge difference between **assuming the risk** and **creating the risk**.

For example, here is a link to a video from a structure fire.

http://www.youtube.com/watch?v=GxFAbks8Sos

First, let me say (as I often do) I am not judging the fire department operating at this scene.

There are plenty of pundits out there who rant from their high perches of judgment, often in non-productive and disrespectful ways. Tuck this lesson away and recall it often: **When we're judging, we cannot be learning**. I hope those who visit my site are here to learn, not to pass judgment.

In the video, the firefighters are performing vertical ventilation at a residential dwelling fire. The fire conditions are significant. It's a little difficult to assess the building construction type but I think it is fair to surmise the structure is well on its way to losing its battle against gravity as a result of the fire weakening the components of construction.

Let's apply the maxim: *We will risk a lot to save a lot.* Will the risk these firefighters took to create a ventilation hole be rewarded with a worthwhile outcome?

Firefighting is risky. Every firefighter knows that. But there is a big difference between **assuming the risk** of a fire and **creating the risk** by performing tasks in ways that are unsafe or inconsistent with best practices and then hiding behind the testosterone-laden mantra: *We're firefighters. That's what we do!*

I am a firefighter too. Well, at least I was one... for 30+ years. But I also had other obligations (roles) that were important to me. I was a husband, a dad, a son, and a brother (both in the biblical and fraternal sense). Maybe I was just a selfish person, but I always did everything in my power to make sure I did not create risk through my behaviors or orders and everyone who was under my command returned home to fulfill their non-firefighter obligations.

It takes a real hero to stand up for safety, especially if surrounded by others who are consumed by their self-anointed *hero* status. Thank you, but I'd rather be a hero to my grandson than to my widow.

A Solution

1. Acknowledge the risks inherit in the work we do.

2. Learn everything possible about how firefighters get hurt and killed by reading near-miss and line-of-duty death reports.

3. Discuss how to manage risk by using best practices.

4. Ensure the risks being taken are worth the potential reward.

5. Train on SOMETHING every day. The way to ensure peak performance is to make incremental improvements over time.

6. Learn from the outcomes. Even when the outcomes are good, ask "Did our actions make sense? What were the potential risks? What was the reward we were trying to accomplish?

Discussion

1. Describe what your department does to support taking appropriate risks based on rewards.

2. If your department had an experience similar to that in the video, how would you learn from it?

3. Have you ever found yourself performing tasks that did not justify the risk? Did you stop or did you continue?

44-DENIAL

I received the following feedback from a subscriber to the monthly Situational Awareness Newsletter. I thought I'd share it and use it as an introduction to this chapter. Here's what he had to say:

I forwarded your newsletter to every one of my email contacts. Your November newsletter was especially appropriate for some of the people on my mailing list because of the article you wrote on Mayday policies. You are going to find this amazing but the training officer for one of our local fire departments does not believe they need a Mayday or RIC policy because as he said "that will never happen here" and "when was the last time we had anything like that happen in this town". I sent the newsletter to him but doubt he will take any action. Let's hope, however, that hearing the message from somebody else besides me will light a fire under his rear end.

Will denial make the problem better or worse?

The question seems rhetorical. The statements of the training officer seems incomprehensible. But I have to share with you, I meet more than my share of firefighters with a similar disposition during my situational awareness and decision making programs. It's sad and unfortunate because I know while I'm sharing the many examples of how firefighters die, these people are sitting there in a defensive, close-minded posture thinking to themselves: *That will never happen here,* and *When was the last time we had anything like that happen in this town.*

One of the keynote programs I deliver is called: *A Recipe from Hell's Kitchen: The ingredients for a perfect catastrophe.* Here's the recipe:

The Recipe from Hell's Kitchen

STEP 1: Take a large helping of *incompetent behavior*.

STEP 2: Remove all the *consequence*.

STEP 3: Cover and allow *confidence* to rise.

STEP 4: Deny the existence of the deadly mixture until *complacency* sets in.

STEP 5: Put into PPE and send into an oven. When PASS Alarms ring the *catastrophe* will be ready.

In next four chapters we will address each component of the Recipe From Hell's Kitchen.

45-THE RECIPE FROM HELL'S KITCHEN – PART 1

I am blessed. My work allows me to uncover many lessons from human behavior and cognitive neuroscience research that benefit the situational awareness of first responders. My 30+ years in fire and EMS positions me well to understand how those lessons can improve our safety. It has truly become my passion and my calling. [This is where you can breath a sigh of relief and be thankful there's a nerd out there who's got your back... taking one for the team so to speak.]

Anyhow... I have evaluated many hundreds of near-miss and casualty incidents. While I enjoying learning and sharing the lessons, it can also be very discouraging and frustrating process. This is especially true when I see common threads that tie casualty incidents together. One of those threads I call *A Recipe from Hell's Kitchen.*

The Recipe from Hell's Kitchen

STEP 1: Take a large helping of ***incompetent behavior***.

STEP 2: Remove all the ***consequence***.

STEP 3: Cover and allow ***confidence*** to rise.

STEP 4: Deny the existence of the deadly mixture until ***complacency*** sets in.

STEP 5: Put into PPE and send into an oven. When PASS Alarms ring the ***catastrophe*** will be ready.

In this chapter we are going to focus on Step 1: Incompetent behavior.

Incompetence

What is incompetent behavior? There are probably many ways to define incompetent behavior. I will define it as behavior that is not consistent with best practices or behaviors that expose personnel to undue risk.

Why would anyone behave incompetently? It's a fair question. I don't think anyone does it on purpose. Or at least I hope no one does it on purpose.

I think what happens more often is responders don't know what best practices are. Perhaps they've never received the training on how to perform in ways consistent with best practices. Maybe they are under-resourced so they're just "doing the best they can with what they have" which means they are at risk for over extending themselves beyond their abilities. The reasons could be a long list and maybe I'll create the list some other time.

One thing I can say with confidence, when most responders behave in ways that are incompetent – they are not doing it on purpose. Hopefully there are few responders who would set out on a purposeful course to be reckless and bring harm to themselves or co-workers with intent. I've certainly not seen that as the motive in the many first responders I have interviewed following their near-miss and casualty event.

Incompetent behavior doesn't look like incompetent behavior at the time it's happening – at least to the person who's doing it. After the fact, however, when the videos, photos and audio tapes start flying around, the behavior may look incompetent.

Those who evaluate and judge the performance of others have the benefit of *hindsight bias* – the ability to look at an event with the benefit of knowing the outcome – then judging those who were performing the tasks (in real-time and without the benefit of knowing what the evaluator now knows are the facts). I think layperson's term for it is *Monday Morning Quarterbacking*.

For those who've attended one of my *Mental Management of Emergencies* programs you know I spend a lot of time talking about each component of this tragic recipe. If you've not had the opportunity to attend the program yet, no worries. I'm going to use this series to provide you a brief view of each step in this deadly recipe.

A Solution

It is tough to give advice about how to fix incompetent behaviors if they don't look incompetent at the time they are occurring. The best advice I can offer is to learn the right way to do things during training and reinforce those best practices over and over again. Avoid taking shortcuts under stress.

Many incidents require quick action. This requires a well-developed situational awareness (which, if you read all the chapters in this book you'll quickly see is what I'm trying to accomplish here).

A second best practice is to look at the task to be performed and think about the outcome (both positive and negative). This is actually one of the essential components of situational awareness – being able to make accurate predications of future events. In neuroscience parlance it's called *Projection* – being able to look ahead of the current moment and see the bad things that may be coming your way. It is also my personal mission: *Helping first responders see the bad things coming in time to change the outcome.*

In the next segment, I'm going to talk about consequences – the bad things that come from incompetent behaviors.

Discussion

1. Have you observed members of your department performing in ways that could be described as incompetent? Why did it happen? Was it corrected?

2. Have you ever found yourself doing a task in a way you thought was a best practice, only to have it not turn out well and looking back (using hindsight) realized your method was flawed?

3. What processes does your department have in place to evaluate operations and to ensure that tactical duties follow best practices?

46-THE RECIPE FROM HELL'S KITCHEN – PART 2

In this Chapter I share the second step of the recipe – consequence. Rather, the lack of consequence and the impact this may have on firefighter situational awareness. One of the outcomes you might expect when there is incompetent behavior is an injury – a consequence. But that is not always the case. Sometimes, no, most of the time, incompetent behavior does not result in a consequence. There's no bad outcome. That, unto itself, is a bad outcome. First, a refresher. Here's the recipe:

The Recipe from Hell's Kitchen

STEP 1: Take a large helping of **incompetent behavior**.

STEP 2: Remove all the **consequence**.

STEP 3: Cover and allow **confidence** to rise.

STEP 4: Deny the existence of the deadly mixture until **complacency** sets in.

STEP 5: Put into PPE and send into an oven. When PASS Alarms ring the **catastrophe** will be ready.

No Consequence

What does it mean to have no consequence? The consequence is the outcome. The problem is when there is no bad outcome as a result of incompetent behavior, the incompetent behavior doesn't look so, well, incompetent. The logical brain starts to rationalize the incompetent behavior as acceptable behavior. The first responder may justify the behavior by thinking: *What I am doing is ok because if it weren't someone would have got hurt. Or, at least, there would have been a near-miss event.*

There are a couple of flaws in this logic, however. First is the confusion of luck with skill. It doesn't take much time surfing YouTube to see there are lots of lucky first responders out there performing in ways that are incompetent. The videos chronicle many incompetent behaviors and show the lack of consequence for the behavior.

If they don't know better, others observing the incompetent behavior in the videos are learning. The mere lack of consequence may cause an observer to see the behavior as acceptable.

Near-Miss Unawareness

Ironically, in a chapter dedicated to improving situational awareness, I am about to talk about unawareness. It is possible that a firefighter performing incompetently can have a near-miss event and be completely unaware of it. The lack of consequence contributes to the unawareness.

To give you an example of this, let's get off the fireground and on to the highway. As you're driving down the road you observe a civilian run a red light, almost causing an accident. The driver who ran the light is talking on his cell phone and he is completely unaware that he almost caused the accident. He just keeps on driving and talking on his phone.

He doesn't even know he had a near-miss because there was no consequence (at least from his point of view). His inattentive driving is, by all accounts, incompetent. He was so distracted by his cell phone conversation that he was unaware of the roadway conditions, unaware that he ran the red light, and unaware that he almost caused an accident.

The same thing can happen where firefighters operating at an emergency scene performing in ways that are incompetent and are completely unaware of it because the consequence is missing. I see this all often in my classes when I ask the question to 100+ firefighters: *Who's had a near miss even in the last six month?* When no hands go up or just one or two hands go up, I know Near-Miss Unawareness is the culprit.

In one class I had a firefighter share that his department has only experienced one near-miss in the past five years when a firefighter fell through a floor, suffered fall and burn injuries, called a mayday, and was successfully rescued. Actually, that's not a near-miss. That's a HIT! (an incident with a significant consequence).

A Solution

It is very important to understand what behaviors are best practices (i.e., competent). This can be done through training by well-trained and well-prepared instructors.

On incident scenes, a safety officer plays a critical role in helping to identify and correct incompetent behaviors before they ever have the opportunity to result in a near-miss or a hit.

When members are watching incident videos (formally or informally) it can be advantageous to have an experienced member present to point out acts of incompetence and the seemingly innocent near-misses, explaining the best practices that would correct the incompetence and sharing the potential consequence to members.

In the next segment, I'm going to talk about confidence – the sense of assurance that results from the performance of incompetent behaviors that lack consequence.

Discussion

1. Describe an activity you've observed that was incompetent, yet lacked consequence.

2. List and describe three incident related near-miss events you've witnessed where those involved did not realize a near-miss had occurred.

3. Have you ever visited the National Firefighter Near Miss Reporting System and used a near-miss event from the system for training your members?

47 - THE RECIPE FROM HELL'S KITCHEN – PART 3

In this Chapter we continue our discussion on *Recipe from Hell's Kitchen* series as I share the third step of the recipe – confidence and more specifically how an overinflated sense of confidence can erode firefighter situational awareness. Confidence is the sense of assurance that results from the performance of duties believed to be high quality. The problem of confidence can rise from the performance of low quality (incompetent) behaviors especially when those incompetent behaviors lack consequence (bad outcomes). This can cause confidence levels to rise and can also cause the evil cousins of confidence to rear their ugly heads – Ego and Arrogance.

The Recipe from Hell's Kitchen

STEP 1: Take a large helping of *incompetent behavior*.

STEP 2: Remove all the *consequence*.

STEP 3: Cover and allow *confidence* to rise.

STEP 4: Deny the existence of the deadly mixture until *complacency* sets in.

STEP 5: Put into PPE and send into an oven. When PASS Alarms ring the *catastrophe* will be ready.

Recall in the previous two chapters I shared how a first responder can behave in a way that is incompetent and not even know it. This unawareness can come from a variety of reasons, one being the lack of consequence (no bad outcome). When these two ingredients are combined (incompetence and lack of consequence) and repeated over and over again it can cause confidence levels to rise, leading the responder to believe the inappropriate behavior is acceptable.

The responder may even believe he or she has discovered a new best practice because the task can be accomplished more efficiently or more effectively than doing it the way it was taught during recruit school.

The combination of these three ingredients can have many unfortunate results. When I have been invited into fire departments following a line-of-duty event, I often uncover the factors that contributed to the casualty were a series of incompetent behaviors (though they did not see them as incompetent) that were being performed over and over again for many years. The department had become comfortable in performing tasks in incompetent ways because there was never a consequence.

There are may terms used for this phenomenon. It is sometimes termed: *The Standardization of Deviant Behavior* – where undesirable behavior becomes the norm because no one sees the behavior as unacceptable. Everyone is too close to the problem to see it. In my classes, I call it *Error Creep* and describe it as the movement toward incompetent behavior over a period of time. The pace is so slow those involved are unaware they are heading (creeping) toward disaster.

Performing incompetently over time without consequence builds confidence and can lull responders into believing their behaviors are now best practices.

They're not... but the responders think they are. It's false confidence. If someone tries to point out their shortcomings, they're likely to be admonished for even suggesting there's a problem with a performance standard that has been successfully used for years. There's little success to be found in arguing with a person whose full of self confidence and arrogance.

Self confidence, left unchecked by reality, can inflate the ego. When someone has found success in the repetition of incompetent behaviors, their sense of self-esteem is high. They become completely comfortable – confident – in the performance of their duties the same way they've always done it and self-assured the results will be the same (good). It can be very difficult to convince them otherwise.

In fact, efforts to convince them their practices may be dangerous is tantamount to trying to teach a pig to sing. You're not going to be successful and you're only going to annoy the pig. The same may be said when trying to convince a responder who has become arrogant as a result of inflated confidence that his or her performance may result in a casualty.

There are abundant examples of this phenomenon documented in casualty reports where the investigators are able to chronicle the presence of flawed performance over long periods of time. The sad things is, when a casualty event does occur, the department and its leaders seem stunned that such a consequence could befall them. They were *doing everything right*. Actually they weren't. But they were blind to their shortcomings. Blinded by confidence, ego and arrogance.

The lack of consequence and the resulting over confidence can also cause responders to let their guards down. When this happens, the responder can stop capturing the clues and cues that are essential to the formation of situational awareness and predictably, situational awareness erodes.

A Solution

One of the ways to hold confidence in check is to continually be conducting self assessments, trying to identify how things can go wrong. This is sometimes termed having a *preoccupation with failure*.

Look at operations and ask how things might turn out poorly if only one or two factors were different (e.g., volume of fire, experience level of the first-in crew, water supply, wind conditions, violent patient, inattentive driver... the list may be endless).

Where bad outcomes are predictable, they can be prevented. However, that requires taking a critical view of performance and identifying where incompetent behaviors exist and fixing them. Expect some pushback. If there hasn't been consequences, few people are going to buy in to the notion that anything needs to change. You know... *If it ain't broken, don't fix it!* Use near-miss and casualty reports to demonstrate how other responders have suffered consequences from doing the very behaviors your organization feels are acceptable.

When using casualty reports as examples, if your responders talk about those agencies who experienced the loss in disrespectful ways, **SOUND THE ALARM BELLS!** Over confidence and arrogance have taken a deep hold in your organization. There's nothing more dangerous than for one to think he or she is above making the mistakes of others.

In the next chapter, I'm going to talk about complacency and what happens when you let your guard down.

Discussion

1. Describe a near-miss or casualty incident your department has suffered and never saw coming because of inflated confidence levels.

2. Pick an incident you've had recently and look at it through the lens of preoccupation with failure. Identify what factors, if only changed slightly, may have caused the incident to result in a casualty.

3. Discuss three ways your department could overcome the trap of inflated confidence, unhealthy egos and arrogance to improve safety.

48-THE RECIPE FROM HELL'S KITCHEN – PART 4

In this Chapter we address for fourth ingredient of the Recipe from Hell's Kitchen – complacency – and more specifically letting your safety guard down and how it can result in failure to learn, implement and practice nationally accepted best practices.

As complacency sets in, an organization can lose its inertia and its desire for continual self-improvement. Members can find themselves resting on their laurels, consumed with confidence and pride for how good they have become. A significant near-miss or a casualty event is the wake-up call.

The Recipe from Hell's Kitchen

STEP 1: Take a large helping of ***incompetent behavior***.

STEP 2: Remove all the **consequence**.

STEP 3: Cover and allow **confidence** to rise.

STEP 4: Deny the existence of the deadly mixture until ***complacency*** sets in.

STEP 5: Put into PPE and send into an oven. When PASS Alarms ring the ***catastrophe*** will be ready.

Recall in the previous three segments I shared how a first responder can behave in a way that is incompetent and, without consequence, it can cause confidence to rise. Left unabated, these ingredients contribute to complacency. Complacency can manifest itself in several ways: Apathy, laziness, and indifference. The surest way to head in the direction of disaster is to have public safety providers who are apathetic, lazy or indifferent.

When responders let down their guard, they significantly raise the risk of having a casualty event. A complacent responder may not even be phased by a near-miss event, even if it results in an injury.

This is different from the scenario I spoke of in a previous segment where a responder is unaware of a near-miss. In this scenario, the responder is aware of the near-miss but simply dismisses it as a chance coincidence or the kind of thing that only happens to someone else.

Complacent responders lack the inertia needed for continual self-improvement. It's almost like they've climbed to the summit of the mountain and now they are content with sitting there for the balance of their career, enjoying the view. Unfortunately, in public safety, complacency is the highway that casualty events travel down looking for a place to happen.

During my safety programs, I sometimes find myself in the presence of a complacent responder and those who are frustrated by the responder who has become complacent. Instructors can spot complacent responders. They act as through the lessons being shared are for the benefit of someone else, not them. Or they see themselves as invincible – believing the bad things only happen to someone else, not them.

The frustrated responders share stories about how some of their co-workers are high-risk providers because they have become complacent, apathetic, lazy or indifferent.

A Solution

This is a very challenging situation because we're talking about traits of human behavior that are difficult to change. Trying to convince a complacent person they need to change is tantamount to convincing a smoker they need to stop smoking. The motivation to change must come from within. One way you can try to accomplish this is to appeal to what is important to the complacent responder. For many of us, that would be family. The important thing is not to assume someone else's passion. Better to ask.

Find a way to tie the need for continual self improvement – training on skills that are consistent to best practices – as a way to ensure they will be able to remain healthy enough to fulfill their passions. If they seem to lack all passion, they may have deeper psychological issues (although I strongly discourage anyone from making an amateur diagnosis).

You may also try to appeal to them by sharing your passions and how it ties into your desire for continual self improvement. Share your passion but don't become a zealot. If you go over the top you may only annoy them and turn them off. Remember the motive is to appeal to them in a positive way.

Another thing you can try is to invite them to participate in training and involve them in small ways, making incremental steps to bring them back into the fold. Remember the journey of a thousand miles begins with one small step.

In the final segment, I'm going to talk about consequence – the bad outcomes that result when the ingredients of the recipe come together and the organization suffers a line-of-duty death.

Discussion

1. Discuss the factors you think contributes to first responder complacency.

2. Share examples you have witnessed where complacency has contributed to a near-miss or casualty events.

3. What strategies do you use to keep from becoming complacent in your training and preparation for peak performance?

49-THE RECIPE FROM HELL'S KITCHEN – PART 5

This is the final chapter dedicated to our discussion about the *Recipe from Hell's Kitchen*. In this chapter I want to share my personal perspectives on the catastrophic outcomes that result when the ingredients of the recipe come together. You may recall in the first chapter in this series I shared with you that I see this recipe being used over and over again in the creation of first responder casualties. Enough so that it makes me sick, literally.

This chapter was the least enjoyable for me to write and I put it off for as long as I could. It may, as well, be the least enjoyable for you to read. Please do not skip it. If we are going to be compassionate leaders of first responders and committed to improving safety, we must take a dose of distasteful medicine on occasion.

The Recipe from Hell's Kitchen

<u>STEP 1</u>: Take a large helping of ***incompetent behavior***.

<u>STEP 2</u>: Remove all the ***consequence***.

<u>STEP 3</u>: Cover and allow ***confidence*** to rise.

<u>STEP 4</u>: Deny the existence of the deadly mixture until ***complacency*** sets in.

<u>STEP 5</u>: Put into PPE and send into an oven. When PASS Alarms ring the ***catastrophe*** will be ready.

Moved beyond words

It was the afternoon of December 20, 1991 and I was in my office at the Springfield Township Fire Department near Akron, Ohio wrapping up some work before taking a long overdue break for the Christmas holiday. My phone rang and the conversation I had led to a question being asked of me that would change my life. It was Chief Clarence Bittner on the other end of the phone.

Bittner was the chief of the Lakemore Fire Department, a community we bordered and provided mutual aid to.

While I was a relatively new chief, we'd developed an amazing working relationship. *"Did you see what happened in Pennsylvania this morning?"* he asked. *"No, I haven't seen any news today."* (Remember, this was before Facebook and Twitter could get news out in a flash).

He told me four firefighters had died fighting a structure fire in Brackenridge. I grew up not far outside of Pittsburgh so I knew where Brackenridge was but I'd never been there. It was tragic news, but I was busy. I had a lot to get done before my Christmas break. Then... came the question that changed my life.

"Have you ever been to the funeral for a firefighter whose been killed in the line of duty?" I hadn't. The closest I had come was attending the funeral of a firefighter/friend from my hometown department who died at home following a fire incident. When I told Chief Bittner I'd not attended a LODD funeral, he said: *"You need to. I'll get the details and get back to you."* Yes, the firefighters' deaths in Brackenridge were tragic. But it was Christmas. I didn't want to attend a funeral at Christmas. Let alone a funeral for people I did not know.

But Bittner insisted I go and I held him in high esteem. He'd been a trusted advisor and was one of the wisest people I'd ever met. If he thought I should go, I would go. It was Christmas Eve and I was at a funeral. While being one of the saddest things I'd ever done in my life, it was at the same time one of the best things I ever done. To this day I remember the vivid details. The grief on the faces of the firefighters and family members is seared into my memory.

While we were standing there in formation, Chief Bittner leaned into me and whispered: *"Rich, do you see how sad everyone is?"* My voice strained and crackled a *"Yes"* as tears rolled down my cheeks. Then he whispered something I will never forget for so long as I live. *"It's our job to make sure this never happens in Springfield and Lakemore."*

I had attended a funeral for four men I did not know who died fighting a structure fire in a town I'd never been to. I didn't even know the circumstances of how they died other than what had been reported on the news. But this 2-hour event changed my life forever.

The investigation

The United States Fire Administration investigates and issues reports on selected major fires. The fire in Brackenridge was among them. Among the observations in the report:

The analysis of this incident provides several valuable lessons for the fire service. Unfortunately these are all revisited lessons, not new discoveries. These firefighters died in the line-of-duty, while conducting operations that appeared to be routine, and were unaware of the situation that was developing below them... This situation bears distinct similarities to other incidents that have claimed the lives of several firefighters in the past.

Sadly, the observations in this report are echoed in countless line-of-duty death reports. In fact, I often say in my programs: *When it comes to firefighters getting killed in structure fires, we're not inventing any new ways to do it. We're simply taking all the ways we already know how to do it and perfecting it by doing them over and over and over again.* It truly makes my heart ache.

The families

The families of the four firefighters were recently interviewed and the article was published on the PittsburghLive.com website. I encourage you to read the article. When you do, pay close attention to what the family members have to say. Imagine how every aspect of life changed on December 21, 1991.

The wife of one of the firefighters was expecting a child. The following spring her son was born. A son who would never know his dad. A son who would never get tucked in at night by his dad. A son who would never toss a ball around the yard with his best friend. A son who would never share a Christmas with dad.

The Catastrophe

Imagine how it must feel for a family when a report is issued that identifies organizational or performance deficiencies that could have changed the outcome. That hurts.

Imagine how it must feel for firefighters who now see, after the fact, the tragedy could have been avoided if steps had been taken to improve safety. That hurts.

The tragedy of a firefighter's death is far reaching and long lasting. I have since attended more firefighter funerals, memorials at the National Fire Academy, and on several occasions been invited in to help fire departments learn and heal from tragic losses. That hurts. In fact, it never stops hurting.

Incompetence. It's the first ingredient in a recipe that can result in tragedy.

Thank you for the gift of your time to read The Recipe From Hell's Kitchen series. I am hopeful the information will be valuable to you in your efforts to improve your safety and the safety of others in your organization. Please remember the process of creating organizational change is one that is best accomplished in small increments over a period of time. Trying to change too much, too fast, can result in push-back and resentment from members who may not be as enthusiastic about changing as you may be. Please let me know how I can help.

50-YOU CAN'T HANDLE THE TRUTH!

If you have attended one of my new Mental Management of Emergencies programs you have learned how stress is a game-changer when it comes to firefighter situational awareness and decision making quality. Most basic training programs focus on developing cognitive knowledge and physical skills. Far less address the impact of stress on situational awareness and decision making and the seemingly irrational (some might even term it bazaar) behaviors manifested under stress.

If you're an avid viewer of the seemingly never ending supply of well-hyped 'raw video' from emergency scenes pervasive on the Internet, you've seen many examples of the irrational behavior of first responders. In this chapter, I'm going to address a behavior manifested, in part, by stress and it can have catastrophic consequences.

Liar Liar Pants on Fire

A powerful exercise I conduct during my Fifty Ways to Kill a First Responder program (the companion program to Mental Management of Emergencies) involves demonstrating that stress increases the propensity for humans to lie.

They don't do it on purpose. In fact, at the start of the exercise I instruct the participants to tell the truth and avoid lying. The exercise plays out in front of a stunned audience who watch participants stand there in front of the room, and in spite of my instructions, lie to each other.

But here's the kicker. The participants don't even know they're lying. That's right. Even though they are saying things that are not true, they are consciously unaware they're doing it. The audience laughs when a participant says something outlandish. The participant laughs along with them, even though they have no idea what's so funny.

It's as though some of the participants are in a trance or hypnotized... something I've been accused of doing on occasion but will continue to deny. If we were not in the presence of friends and colleagues, this type of exercise might be a royal embarrassment for the participant.

Everyone in the room gets to see the participants lie, but no one really understands WHY they're lying – especially when I was so emphatic in my instructions that they tell the truth. The answer to the mystery resides in the brain and its powerful need to make sense of this complex world we live in.

The participants in my exercise are told a story that contains about nine pieces of information, surrounded by a bunch of other words to make the sentences run coherently together (I'll call all those unnecessary words *noise*). Only two or three pieces of the information are truly important but the participants don't know which pieces are important and which are not. So they try to remember all of them. How do they do? They fail... miserably. They are suffering from cognitive overload and their poor brains are confused.

Your helpful brain

What the brain does to reconcile the problem of overload can have catastrophic consequences. Like water overflowing the top of a glass, the brain starts shedding information – forgetting if you will. You may be surprised to learn you have about as much control over which pieces of information you'll forget as you would have over which droplets of water run over the rim of the glass and spill on to the table.

Our logical minds want to have us believing that participants will shelve the unimportant information and remember the most important information. But that's not what happens. What does happen leaves the observers stunned. They remember the noise and forget the most important details.

I have conducted this exercise over a hundred times and the outcome is always predictably similar. Because the human brain has a limited capacity to process and recall information, it may be no surprise that information is going to be forgotten. But observers never expect the critical information to be forgotten. But it is.

Confabulation

The second most stunning outcome of this exercise is the participants start to lie. Since lying is often associated with someone who is telling an untruth on purpose (usually to keep from getting into trouble), we think of liars as having purposeful intent to be untruthful. And since these participants are not lying on purpose, we're uncomfortable calling it *lying*. Well, apparently so is the scientific community. Researchers don't like to call it lying either so they made up their own word to describe what's happening.

The participant is doing what is called *confabulation.* In scientific parlance it means the participant's brain is fabricating imaginary stories to compensate for his or her loss of memory. In layperson's terms, you might call it making up a story – or lying.

The loss of memory comes from two sources. Stress and information overload – two ingredients abundant on an emergency scene, right?

Making up stories is a safety mechanism of the brain to help you make sense of the world. If you lack the facts to make a story flow coherently, your brain will use imagination to fill in the missing information. It makes it up as it goes and the story will make sense to the story teller and they will be completely unaware they are confabulating. They tell the story, literally, as if it were fact.

The title of this chapter is *You can't handle the truth.* But it more aptly could be called: *You can't handle the information... so you make up the truth.*

On the emergency scene

So what does this benign classroom exercise have to do with first responder safety? A lot! The same vulnerabilities of the mind played out in the classroom can manifest themselves at an emergency scene.

1. Responders can think things happened that never did.

2. Commanders can believe they gave orders that were never communicated.

3. Responders can recount performing tasks that were never performed.

4. Conditions can be described in ways that are inconsistent with reality.

Good grief! Stress and information overload makes us vulnerable creatures.

A solution

It's important to understand your vulnerabilities. Awareness of your shortcomings is the first step toward managing them. Situational awareness is an important ingredient in managing this cognitive shortcoming. Here's why.

Level 1 situational awareness is developed by a constant scanning of the environment for clues and cues (information). But not every piece of information is important.

Scan and search for the most important pieces that will help with good decision making, much like you would scan a thousand pieces of a unassembled jigsaw puzzle to find the four corners.

Level 2 situational awareness is understanding the meaning of the information. Factual, timely information, in limited quantities, is key to comprehension. Volumes of information are not the friend of a stressed brain. In fact, it's the basis for confabulation.

Level 3 situational awareness is being able to predict the future events. In order to do that, one must have an accurate understanding of the current events. Meaning, Level 3 situational awareness (SA) is built on the successful development of Level 1 SA and Level 2 SA. It all starts with capturing the right quantity and quality of information and knowing how to sift through the noise.

Discussion

1. Discuss a time when you, or someone you know, confabulated a story without realizing it was untrue.

2. If you are a parent (or if you aren't, think back to when you were a kid) and discuss an example of childhood confabulation. (Remember, the motive is NOT to tell an untruth to keep from getting into trouble – that is lying!)

3. Discuss an emergency incident where you truly thought something happened or something was said in a certain way only to find out later you had confabulated.

4. Describe what happens to you when you try to process to many pieces of information at an emergency scene?

PROLOGUE

Serving your community as a first responder is both a great honor and a tremendous responsibility. Citizens depend on you to be well-trained and well-prepared to handle their emergencies. It is a noble calling.

First responders have been blessed with tremendous advancements in equipment and in training, yet there are still hundreds of first responders killed every year in traumatic injuries at emergency scenes, struck at roadway incidents and in violent attacks.

My mission is to help you see the bad things coming in time to change the outcome. I have dedicated my life to this cause. Please let me know how I can help you.

ABOUT THE AUTHOR

Dr. Gasaway is a fire service professional with more than 30 years experience, including 22 years as a chief officer and incident commander. He is considered to be one of the nation's leading authorities on public safety decision making and situational awareness in high-stress, high consequence environments.

Dr. Gasaway's contributions have been featured in more than 450 journal articles, books, book chapters, videos, podcasts, webinars and research projects on topics related to emergency services leadership, decision making, incident management and training.

His programs are noted for providing strong content that are immediately usable by first responders. Dr. Gasaway's presentation style has been described as "must-see" by seminar and keynote attendees - "a cross between a nerdy neuro-researcher and a stand-up comic." It's effective! And puts him in high-demand.

Dr. Gasaway has delivered over 4,000 presentations to more than 54,000 first responders from the United States, Canada, England, Australia and Hong Kong.

CONTACT THE AUTHOR

If you are interested in hosting a program, please contact Dr. Gasaway at:

Rich@RichGasaway.com

Please consider visiting my websites. There is a treasure trove full of free stuff. And, hey, who doesn't like free stuff, right?

Situational Awareness Matters!
www.SAMatters.com

Gasaway Consulting Group
www.RichGasaway.com

Here are some other ways we can get connected:

Office: 612-548-4424

Facebook: www.Facebook.com/groups/SAMatters

Twitter: @RichGasaway

YouTube: SAMattersTV

Made in the USA
Columbia, SC
03 August 2021